Basic Chemistry

Student Solutions Manual

7th Edition

Steven S. Zumdahl

CENGAGE
Learning™

Australia • Brazil • Japan • Korea • Mexico • Singapore • Spain • United Kingdom • United States

Basic Chemistry: Student Solutions Manual, 7th Edition

Basic Chemistry: Student Solutions Manual, 7th Edition
Hall
© 2011 Cengage Learning. All rights reserved.

Executive Editors:
Maureen Staudt
Michael Stranz

Senior Project Development Manager:
Linda deStefano

Marketing Specialist:
Courtney Sheldon

Senior Production/Manufacturing Manager:
Donna M. Brown

PreMedia Manager:
Joel Brennecke

Sr. Rights Acquisition Account Manager:
Todd Osborne

Cover Image:
Getty Images*

*Unless otherwise noted, all cover images used by Custom Solutions, a part of Cengage Learning, have been supplied courtesy of Getty Images with the exception of the Earthview cover image, which has been supplied by the National Aeronautics and Space Administration (NASA).

For product information and technology assistance, contact us at
Cengage Learning Customer & Sales Support, 1-800-354-9706

For permission to use material from this text or product, submit all requests online at **cengage.com/permissions**
Further permissions questions can be emailed to
permissionrequest@cengage.com

This book contains select works from existing Cengage Learning resources and was produced by Cengage Learning Custom Solutions for collegiate use. As such, those adopting and/or contributing to this work are responsible for editorial content accuracy, continuity and completeness.

Compilation © 2011 Cengage Learning
ISBN-13: 978-1-133-06879-2

ISBN-10: 1-133-06879-0

Cengage Learning
5191 Natorp Boulevard
Mason, Ohio 45040
USA
Cengage Learning is a leading provider of customized learning solutions with office locations around the globe, including Singapore, the United Kingdom, Australia, Mexico, Brazil, and Japan. Locate your local office at:
international.cengage.com/region.

Cengage Learning products are represented in Canada by Nelson Education, Ltd.
For your lifelong learning solutions, visit **www.cengage.com/custom.**
Visit our corporate website at **www.cengage.com.**

Printed in the United States of America

Contents

Preface

This guide contains the even-numbered solutions for the end-of-chapter problems in the seventh editions of *Introductory Chemistry, Introductory Chemistry: A Foundation*, and *Basic Chemistry* by Steven S. Zumdahl and Donald J. DeCoste. Several hundred new problems and questions have been prepared for the new editions of the text, which we hope will be of even greater help to students in gaining an understanding of the fundamental principles of chemistry.

We have tried to give the most detailed solutions possible to all the problems, even though some problems give repeat drill practice on the same subject. Our chief attempt at brevity is to give molar masses for compounds without showing the calculation (after the subject of molar mass itself has been discussed). We have also made a conscious effort in this guide to solve each problem in the manner discussed in the textbook. The instructor, of course, may wish to discuss alternative methods of solution with his or her students.

One topic that causes many students concern is the matter of significant figures and the determination of the number of digits to which a solution to a problem should be reported. To avoid truncation errors in the solutions contained in this guide, the solutions typically report intermediate answers to one more digit than appropriate for the final answer. The final answer to each problem is then given to the correct number of significant figures based on the data provided in the problem.

I wish you the best of luck and success in your study of chemistry!

James F. Hall

University of Massachusetts Lowell

CHAPTER 1

Chemistry: An Introduction

2.   The answer will depend on student examples.

4.   Answer depends on student responses/examples.

6.   This answer depends on your own experience, but consider the following examples: oven cleaner (the label says it contains sodium hydroxide; it converts the burned-on grease in the oven to a soapy material that washes away); drain cleaner (the label says it contains sodium hydroxide; it dissolves the clog of hair in the drain); stomach antacid (the label says it contains calcium carbonate; it makes me belch and makes my stomach feel better); hydrogen peroxide (the label says it is a 3% solution of hydrogen peroxide; when applied to a wound, it bubbles); depilatory cream (the label says it contains sodium hydroxide; it removes unwanted hair from skin).

8.   The scientist must recognize the problem and state it clearly, propose possible solutions or explanations, and then decide through experimentation which solution or explanation is best.

10.   Answer depends on student response. A quantitative observation must include a number. For example "There are two windows in this room" represents a quantitative observation, but "The walls of this room are yellow" is a qualitative observation.

12.   Answer depends on student responses/examples.

14.   Chemistry is not just a set of facts that have to be memorized. To be successful in chemistry, you have to be able to apply what you have learned to new situations, new phenomena, and new experiments. Rather than just learning a list of facts or studying someone else's solution to a problem, your instructor hopes you will learn *how* to solve problems *yourself,* so that you will be able to apply what you have learned in future circumstances.

16.   In real life situations, the problems and applications likely to be encountered are not simple textbook examples. One must be able to observe an event, hypothesize a cause, and then test this hypothesis. One must be able to carry what has been learned in class forward to new, different situations.

CHAPTER 2

Measurements and Calculations

2. "Scientific notation" means we have to put the decimal point after the first significant figure, and then express the order of magnitude of the number as a power of ten. So we want to put the decimal point after the first 2:

    $2,421 \rightarrow 2.421 \times 10^{\text{to some power}}$

    To be able to move the decimal point three places to the left in going from 2,421 to 2.421, means I will need a power of 10^3 after the number, where the exponent 3 shows that I moved the decimal point 3 places to the left.

    $2,421 \rightarrow 2.421 \times 10^{\text{to some power}} = 2.421 \times 10^3$

4. a. 10^4

    b. 10^{-3}

    c. 10^2

    d. 10^{-30}

6. a. negative

    b. zero

    c. positive

    d. negative

8. a. The decimal point must be moved three spaces to the right: 2789

    b. The decimal point must be moved three spaces to the left: 0.002789

    c. The decimal point must be moved seven spaces to the right: 93,000,000.

    d. The decimal point must be moved one space to the right: 42.89.

    e. The decimal point must be moved 4 spaces to the right: 99,990.

    f. The decimal point must be moved 5 spaces to the left: 0.00009999.

10. a. three spaces to the left

    b. one space to the left

    c. five spaces to the right

    d. one space to the left

    e. two spaces to the right

    f. two spaces to the left

12. a. The decimal point must be moved 3 places to the right: 6244

  b. The decimal point must be moved 2 spaces to the left: 0.09117

  c. The decimal point must be moved 1 space to the right: 82.99

  d. The decimal point must be moved 4 spaces to the left: 0.0001771

  e. The decimal point must be moved 2 spaces to the right: 545.1

  f. The decimal point must be moved 5 spaces to the left: 0.00002934

14. a. $1/0.00032 = 3.1 \times 10^3$

  b. $10^3/10^{-3} = 1 \times 10^6$

  c. $10^3/10^3 = 1$ (1×10^0); any number divided by itself is unity.

  d. $1/55,000 = 1.8 \times 10^{-5}$

  e. $(10^5)(10^4)(10^{-4})/10^{-2} = 1 \times 10^7$

  f. $43.2/(4.32 \times 10^{-5}) = \dfrac{4.32 \times 10^1}{4.32 \times 10^{-5}} = 1.00 \times 10^6$

  g. $(4.32 \times 10^{-5})/432 = \dfrac{4.32 \times 10^{-5}}{4.32 \times 10^2} = 1.00 \times 10^{-7}$

  h. $1/(10^5)(10^{-6}) = 1/(10^{-1}) = 1 \times 10^1$

16. The metric system uses prefixes to indicate multiples of the basic SI units. For example, a *centi*meter is $\frac{1}{100}$ of a meter; a *kilo*meter is 1000 meters.

18. Since a pound is 453.6 grams, the 125-g can will be slightly more than ¼ pound.

20. Since 1 inch = 2.54 cm, the nail is approximately an inch long.

22. Since a liter is slightly more than a quart, the 2–liter bottle is larger.

24. 1.62 m is approximately 5 ft, 4 in. The woman is slightly taller.

26. a. centimeter

  b. meter

  c. kilometer

28. d (the other units would give very large numbers for the distance).

30. When we use a measuring device with an analog scale, we estimate the reading to 0.1 of the smallest scale divisions on the measuring scale. Since this last reading is decided by the user, not by the divisions on the measuring scale, the final digit of the measurement is uncertain no matter how careful we may be in making the determination.

32. The scale of the ruler shown is only marked to the nearest *tenth* of a centimeter; writing 2.850 would imply that the scale was marked to the nearest *hundredth* of a centimeter (and that the zero in the thousandths place had been estimated).

34.   a.   three (the relationship is exact)

       b.   two (a counting number)

       c.   five (

       d.   only two since there is no decimal point indicated

36.   It is better to round off only the final answer, and to carry through extra digits in intermediate calculations. If there are enough steps to the calculation, rounding off in each step may lead to a cumulative error in the final answer.

38.   a. 4.18×10^{-6}

       b. 3.87×10^{4}

       c. 9.11×10^{-30}

       d. 5.46×10^{6}

40.   a. 8.8×10^{-4}

       b. 9.375×10^{4}

       c. 8.97×10^{-1}

       d. 1.00×10^{3}

42.   The total mass would be determined by the number of decimal places available on the readout of the scale/balance. For example, if a balance whose readout is to the nearest 0.01 g were used, the total mass would be reported to the second decimal place. For example 32.05 g + 29.15 g + 31.09 g would be reported as 92.29 g to the second decimal place. For the calculation 44.05 g + 33.91 g + 48.38 g, the sum would be reported as 126.34 g (a total of five significant figures, but given to the second decimal place).

44.   Most calculators would display 0.66666666. If the 2 and 3 were *experimentally determined* numbers, this quotient would imply far too many significant figures.

46.   none (10,434 is only known to the nearest whole number)

48.   a.   2.3 (the answer can only be given to two significant figures because 3.1 is only known to two significant figures)

       b. 9.1×10^{2}: (the answer can only be given to the first decimal place because 4.1 is only given to the first decimal place; both numbers have the same power of ten)

       c. 1.323×10^{3}: (the numbers must be first expressed as the same power of ten; $1.091 \times 10^{3} + 0.221 \times 10^{3} + 0.0114 \times 10^{3} = 1.323 \times 10^{3}$)

       d. 6.63×10^{-13} (the answer can only be given to three significant figures because 4.22×10^{6} is only given to three significant figures)

50.   a.   one (the factor of 2 has only one significant figure)

       b.   four (the sum within the parentheses will contain four significant figures)

       c.   two (based on the factor 4.7×10^{-6} only having two significant figures)

       d.   three (based on the factor 63.9 having only three significant figures)

52. a. $(2.0944 + 0.0003233 + 12.22)/7.001 = (14.31)/7.001 = 2.045$

    b. $(1.42 \times 10^2 + 1.021 \times 10^3)/(3.1 \times 10^{-1}) =$

    $(142 + 1021)/(3.1 \times 10^{-1}) = (1163)/(3.1 \times 10^{-1}) = 3752 = 3.8 \times 10^3$

    c. $(9.762 \times 10^{-3})/(1.43 \times 10^2 + 4.51 \times 10^1) =$

    $(9.762 \times 10^{-3})/(143 + 45.1) = (9.762 \times 10^{-3})/(188.1) = 5.19 \times 10^{-5}$

    d. $(6.1982 \times 10^{-4})^2 = (6.1982 \times 10^{-4})(6.1982 \times 10^{-4}) = 3.8418 \times 10^{-7}$

54. an infinite number (a definition)

56. $\dfrac{2.54 \text{ cm}}{1 \text{ in}}$ and $\dfrac{1 \text{ in}}{2.54 \text{ cm}}$

58. $\dfrac{1 \text{ lb}}{\$0.79}$

60. a. $4.21 \text{ ft} \times \dfrac{12 \text{ in}}{1 \text{ ft}} = 50.5 \text{ in}$

    b. $37.3 \text{ in} \times \dfrac{1 \text{ ft}}{12 \text{ in}} = 3.11 \text{ ft}$

    c. $45.2 \text{ cm} \times \dfrac{10 \text{ mm}}{1 \text{ cm}} = 452 \text{ mm}$

    d. $761.2 \text{ mm} \times \dfrac{1 \text{ cm}}{10 \text{ mm}} = 76.12 \text{ cm}$

    e. $1.25 \text{ L} \times \dfrac{1.0567 \text{ qt}}{1 \text{ L}} = 1.32 \text{ qt}$

    f. $4.21 \text{ qt} \times \dfrac{2 \text{ pt}}{1 \text{ qt}} = 8.42 \text{ pt}$

    g. $6.21 \text{ kg} \times \dfrac{2.2046 \text{ lb}}{1 \text{ kg}} = 13.7 \text{ lb}$

    h. $1.75 \text{ lb} \times \dfrac{16 \text{ oz}}{1 \text{ lb}} = 28.0 \text{ oz}$

62. a. $104.971 \text{ kPa} \times \dfrac{1 \text{ atm}}{101.325 \text{ kPa}} = 1.03598 \text{ atm}$

    b. $6.25 \text{ pt} \times \dfrac{1 \text{ qt}}{2 \text{ pt}} = 3.13 \text{ qt}$

    c. $18.0 \text{ oz} \times \dfrac{1 \text{ lb}}{16 \text{ oz}} \times \dfrac{1 \text{ kg}}{2.2046 \text{ lb}} = 0.510 \text{ kg}$

d. $4.213 \text{ J} \times \dfrac{1 \text{ cal}}{4.184 \text{ J}} = 1.007 \text{ cal}$

e. $1.632 \text{ mi} \times \dfrac{5280 \text{ ft}}{1 \text{ mi}} = 8617 \text{ ft}$

f. $4.52 \text{ qt} \times \dfrac{2 \text{ pt}}{1 \text{ qt}} = 9.04 \text{ qt}$

g. $9.25 \text{ oz} \times \dfrac{453.59 \text{ g}}{16 \text{ oz}} = 262 \text{ g}$

h. $56.2 \text{ fl oz} \times \dfrac{1 \text{ qt}}{32 \text{ fl oz}} = 1.76 \text{ qt}$

64. $2558 \text{ mi} \times \dfrac{1.6093 \text{ km}}{1 \text{ mi}} = 4117 \text{ km}$

66. $1 \times 10^{-10} \text{ m} \times \dfrac{100 \text{ cm}}{1 \text{ m}} = 1 \times 10^{-8} \text{ cm}$

   $1 \times 10^{-8} \text{ cm} \times \dfrac{1 \text{ in}}{2.54 \text{ cm}} = 4 \times 10^{-9} \text{ in.}$

   $1 \times 10^{-8} \text{ cm} \times \dfrac{1 \text{ m}}{100 \text{ cm}} \times \dfrac{10^{9} \text{ nm}}{1 \text{ m}} = 0.1 \text{ nm}$

68. freezing

70. 273

72. Fahrenheit (F)

74. $T_K = T_C + 273 \qquad T_C = T_K - 273$

   a. $-78.1 + 273 = 194.9 \text{ K } (195 \text{ K})$

   b. $775 \text{ K} - 273 = 502 °\text{C}$

   c. $489 \text{ K} - 273 = 216 °\text{C}$

   d. $24.3 °\text{C} + 273 = 297.3 \text{ K } (297 \text{ K})$

76. $T_F = 1.80(T_C) + 32$

   a. $1.80(78.1) + 32 = 173 °\text{F}$

   b. $1.80(40.) + 32 = 104 °\text{F}$

   c. $1.80(-273) + 32 = -459 °\text{F}$

   d. $1.80(32) + 32 = 90. °\text{F}$

78. $T_F = 1.80(T_C) + 32$ $T_C = (T_F - 32)/1.80$ $T_K = T_C + 273$

a. $275 - 273 = 2°C$

b. $(82 - 32)/1.80 = 28°C$

c. $1.80(-21) + 32 = -5.8°F (-6°F)$

d. $(-40 - 32)/1.80 = -40 °C$ (Celsius and Fahrenheit temperatures are the same at -40).

80. g/cm^3 (g/mL)

82. 100 in.^{3}

84.   Density is a *characteristic* property, which is always the same for a pure substance.

86.   copper

88. $density = \dfrac{mass}{volume}$

a. $d = \dfrac{122.4 \text{ g}}{5.5 \text{ cm}^3} = 22 \text{ g/cm}^3$

b. $v = 0.57 \text{ m}^3 \times \left(\dfrac{100 \text{ cm}}{1 \text{ m}}\right)^3 = 5.7 \times 10^5 \text{ cm}^3$

$d = \dfrac{1.9302 \times 10^4 \text{ g}}{5.7 \times 10^5 \text{ cm}} = 0.034 \text{ g/cm}^3$

c. $m = 0.0175 \text{ kg} \times \dfrac{1000 \text{ g}}{1 \text{ kg}} = 17.5 \text{ g}$

$d = \dfrac{17.5 \text{ g}}{18.2 \text{ mL}} = 0.962 \text{ g/mL} = 0.962 \text{ g/cm}^3$

d. $v = 0.12 \text{ m}^3 \times \left(\dfrac{100 \text{ cm}}{1 \text{ m}}\right)^3 = 1.2 \times 10^5 \text{ cm}^3$

$d = \dfrac{2.49 \text{ g}}{1.2 \times 10^5 \text{ cm}^3} = 2.1 \times 10^{-5} \text{ g/cm}^3$

90. $3.75 \text{ L} = 3750 \text{ mL}$

$3750 \text{ mL} \times \dfrac{0.785 \text{ g}}{1 \text{ ml}} = 2944 \text{ g} = 2.94 \times 10^3 \text{ g}$

$125 \text{ g} \times \dfrac{1 \text{ mL}}{0.785 \text{ g}} = 159 \text{ mL}$

92. $m = 3.5 \text{ lb} \times \dfrac{453.59 \text{ g}}{1 \text{ lb}} = 1.59 \times 10^3 \text{ g}$

$v = 1.2 \times 10^4 \text{ in.}^3 \times \left(\dfrac{2.54 \text{ cm}}{1 \text{ in}}\right)^3 = 1.97 \times 10^5 \text{ cm}^3$

$d = \dfrac{1.59 \times 10^3 \text{ g}}{1.97 \times 10^5 \text{ cm}^3} = 8.1 \times 10^{-3} \text{ g/cm}^3$

The material will float.

94. $5.25 \text{ g} \times \dfrac{1 \text{ cm}^3}{10.5 g} = 0.500 \text{ cm}^3 = 0.500 \text{ mL}$

$11.2 \text{ mL} + 0.500 \text{ mL} = 11.7 \text{ mL}$

96. a. $50.0 \text{ cm}^3 \times \dfrac{19.32 \text{ g}}{1 \text{ cm}^3} = 966 \text{ g}$

b. $50.0 \text{ cm}^3 \times \dfrac{7.87 \text{ g}}{1 \text{ cm}^3} = 394 \text{ g}$

c. $50.0 \text{ cm}^3 \times \dfrac{11.34 \text{ g}}{1 \text{ cm}^3} = 567 \text{ g}$

d. $50.0 \text{ cm}^3 \times \dfrac{2.70 \text{ g}}{1 \text{ cm}^3} = 135 \text{ g}$

98. a. $3.011 \times 10^{23} = 301,100,000,000,000,000,000,000$

b. $5.091 \times 10^9 = 5,091,000,000$

c. $7.2 \times 10^2 = 720$

d. $1.234 \times 10^5 = 123,400$

e. $4.32002 \times 10^{-4} = 0.000432002$

f. $3.001 \times 10^{-2} = 0.03001$

g. $2.9901 \times 10^{-7} = 0.00000029901$

h. $4.2 \times 10^{-1} = 0.42$

100. a. centimeters

b. meters

c. kilometers

d. centimeters

e. millimeters

102.   a. $36.2 \text{ blim} \times \dfrac{1400 \text{ kryll}}{1 \text{ blim}} = 5.07 \times 10^4 \text{ kryll}$

  b. $170 \text{ kryll} \times \dfrac{1 \text{ blim}}{1400 \text{ kryll}} = 0.12 \text{ blim}$

  c. $72.5 \text{ kryll}^2 \times \left(\dfrac{1 \text{ blim}}{1400 \text{ kryll}}\right)^2 = 3.70 \times 10^{-5} \text{ blim}^2$

104. $52 \text{ cm} \times \dfrac{1 \text{ in}}{2.54 \text{ cm}} = 20. \text{ in.}$

106. $1 \text{ lb} \times \dfrac{1 \text{ kg}}{2.2 \text{ lb}} \times \dfrac{\$1.20}{1 \text{ euro}} \times \dfrac{2.45 \, euro}{1 \text{ kg}} = = \$1.33 \text{ per pound}$

108. $°X = 1.26°C + 14$

110. $d = \dfrac{36.8 \text{ g}}{10.5 \text{ L}} = 3.50 \text{ g/L} \quad (3.50 \times 10^{-3} \text{ g/cm}^3)$

112.   For ethanol, $100. \text{ mL} \times \dfrac{0.785 \text{ g}}{1 \text{ mL}} = 78.5 \text{ g}$

  For benzene, $1000 \text{ mL} \times \dfrac{0.880 \text{ g}}{1 \text{ mL}} = 880. \text{ g}$

  total mass, $78.5 + 880. = 959 \text{ g}$

114.   a.   negative
  b.   negative
  c.   positive
  d.   zero
  e.   negative

116.   a.   2; positive
  b.   11; negative
  c.   3; positive
  d.   5; negative
  e.   5; positive
  f.   0; zero
  g.   1; negative
  h.   7; negative

118.   a.   1; positive

    b.   3; negative

    c.   0; zero

    d.   3; positive

    e.   9; negative

120.   a.   The decimal point must be moved five places to the left; $2.98 \times 10^{-5} = 0.0000298$.

    b.   The decimal point must be moved nine places to the right; $4.358 \times 10^{9} = 4,358,000,000$.

    c.   The decimal point must be moved six places to the left; $1.9928 \times 10^{-6} = 0.0000019928$.

    d.   The decimal point must be moved 23 places to the right; $6.02 \times 10^{23} =$ 602,000,000,000,000,000,000,000.

    e.   The decimal point must be moved one place to the left; $1.01 \times 10^{-1} = 0.101$.

    f.   The decimal point must be moved three places to the left; $7.87 \times 10^{-3} = 0.00787$.

    g.   The decimal point must be moved seven places to the right; $9.87 \times 10^{7} = 98,700,000$.

    h.   The decimal point must be moved two places to the right; $3.7899 \times 10^{2} = 378.99$.

    i.   The decimal point must be moved one place to the left; $1.093 \times 10^{-1} = 0.1093$.

    j.   The decimal point must be moved zero places; $2.9004 \times 10^{0} = 2.9004$.

    k.   The decimal point must be moved four places to the left; $3.9 \times 10^{-4} = 0.00039$.

    l.   The decimal point must be moved eight places to the left; $1.904 \times 10^{-8} = 0.00000001904$.

122.   a. $1/10^{2} = 1 \times 10^{-2}$

    b. $1/10^{-2} = 1 \times 10^{2}$

    c. $55/10^{3} = \dfrac{5.5 \times 10^{1}}{1 \times 10^{3}} = 5.5 \times 10^{-2}$

    d. $(3.1 \times 10^{6})/10^{-3} = \dfrac{3.1 \times 10^{6}}{1 \times 10^{-3}} = 3.1 \times 10^{9}$

    e. $(10^{6})^{1/2} = 1 \times 10^{3}$

    f. $(10^{6})(10^{4})/(10^{2}) = \dfrac{(1 \times 10^{6})(1 \times 10^{4})}{(1 \times 10^{2})} = 1 \times 10^{8}$

    g. $1/0.0034 = \dfrac{1}{3.4 \times 10^{-3}} = 2.9 \times 10^{2}$

    h. $3.453/10^{-4} = \dfrac{3.453}{1 \times 10^{-4}} = 3.453 \times 10^{4}$

124.   Kelvin, K

126.   centimeter

128.   0.105 m

130.   1 kg (100 g = 0.1 kg)

132.   10 cm (1 cm = 10 mm)

134.   2.8 (the hundredths place is estimated)

136.   a.   0.000426

     b. 4.02×10^{-5}

     c. 5.99×10^{6}

     d.   400.

     e.   0.00600

138.   a.   2149.6 (the answer can only be given to the first decimal place, because 149.2 is only known to the first decimal place)

     b. 5.37×10^{3} (the answer can only be given to two decimal places because 4.34 is only known to two decimal places; moreover, since the power of ten is the same for each number, the calculation can be performed directly)

     c.   Before performing the calculation, the numbers have to be converted so that they contain the same power of ten.

$4.03 \times 10^{-2} - 2.044 \times 10^{-3} = 4.03 \times 10^{-2} - 0.2044 \times 10^{-2} = 3.83 \times 10^{-2}$ (the answer can only be given the second decimal place because 4.03×10^{-2} is only known to the second decimal place)

     d.   Before performing the calculation, the numbers have to be converted so that they contain the same power of ten.

$2.094 \times 10^{5} - 1.073 \times 10^{6} = 2.094 \times 10^{5} - 10.73 \times 10^{5} = -8.64 \times 10^{5}$

140.   a. $(2.9932 \times 10^{4})(2.4443 \times 10^{2} + 1.0032 \times 10^{1}) =$

$(2.9932 \times 10^{4})(24.443 \times 10^{1} + 1.0032 \times 10^{1}) =$

$(2.9932 \times 10^{4})(25.446 \times 10^{1}) = 7.6166 \times 10^{6}$

     b. $(2.34 \times 10^{2} + 2.443 \times 10^{-1})/(0.0323) =$

$(2.34 \times 10^{2} + 0.002443 \times 10^{2})/(0.0323) =$

$(2.34 \times 10^{2})/(0.0323) = 7.24 \times 10^{3}$

     c. $(4.38 \times 10^{-3})^{2} = 1.92 \times 10^{-5}$

     d. $(5.9938 \times 10^{-6})^{1/2} = 2.4482 \times 10^{-3}$

142. $\dfrac{1 \text{ year}}{12 \text{ months}}; \dfrac{12 \text{ months}}{1 \text{ year}}$

144. a. $908 \text{ oz} \times \dfrac{1 \text{ lb}}{16 \text{ oz}} \times \dfrac{1 \text{ kg}}{2.2046 \text{ lb}} = 25.7 \text{ kg}$

    b. $12.8 \text{ L} \times \dfrac{1 \text{ qt}}{0.94633 \text{ L}} \times \dfrac{1 \text{ gal}}{4 \text{ qt}} = 3.38 \text{ gal}$

    c. $125 \text{ mL} \times \dfrac{1 \text{ L}}{1000 \text{ mL}} \times \dfrac{1 \text{ qt}}{0.94633 \text{ L}} = 0.132 \text{ qt}$

    d. $2.89 \text{ gal} \times \dfrac{4 \text{ qt}}{1 \text{ gal}} \times \dfrac{1 \text{ L}}{1.0567 \text{ qt}} \times \dfrac{1000 \text{ mL}}{1 \text{ L}} = 1.09 \times 10^4 \text{ mL}$

    e. $4.48 \text{ lb} \times \dfrac{453.59 \text{ g}}{1 \text{ lb}} = 2.03 \times 10^3 \text{ g}$

    f. $550 \text{ mL} \times \dfrac{1 \text{ L}}{1000 \text{ mL}} \times \dfrac{1.0567 \text{ qt}}{1 \text{ L}} = 0.58 \text{ qt}$

146. Assuming exactly 6 gross, 864 pencils

148. a. Celsius temperature = $(175 - 32)/1.80 = 79.4°C$

       Kelvin temperature = $79.4 + 273 = 352 \text{ K}$

    b. $255 - 273 = -18 \text{ °C}$

    c. $(-45 - 32)/1.80 = -43°C$

    d. $1.80(125) + 32 = 257°F$

150. $85.5 \text{ mL} \times \dfrac{0.915 \text{ g}}{1 \text{ mL}} = 78.2 \text{ g}$

152. $m = 155 \text{ lb} \times \dfrac{453.59 \text{ g}}{1 \text{ lb}} = 7.031 \times 10^4 \text{ g}$

    $v = 4.2 \text{ ft}^3 \times \left(\dfrac{12 \text{ in}}{1 \text{ ft}}\right)^3 \times \left(\dfrac{2.54 \text{ cm}}{1 \text{ in}}\right)^3 = 1.189 \times 10^5 \text{ cm}^3$

    $d = \dfrac{7.031 \times 10^4 \text{ g}}{1.189 \times 10^5 \text{ cm}^3} = 0.59 \text{ g/cm}^3$

154. $T_F = 1.80(T_C) + 32$

    a. 23 °F

    b. 32 °F

    c. -321 °F

    d. -459 °F

    e. 187 °F

    f. -459 °F

156. a.   The Mars Climate Orbiter dipped 100 km lower in the Mars atmosphere than was planned. Using the conversion factor between miles and kilometers found inside the cover of this text

$$100 \text{ km} \times \frac{1 \text{ mi}}{1.6093 \text{ km}} = 62 \text{ mi}$$

   b.   The aircraft required 22,300 kg of fuel, but only 22,300 lb of fuel was loaded. Using the conversion factor between pounds and kilograms found inside the cover of this text, the amount of fuel required in pounds was

$$22{,}300 \text{ kg} \times \frac{2.2046 \text{ lb}}{1 \text{ kg}} = 49{,}163 \text{ lb}$$

   Therefore, $(49{,}163 - 22{,}300) = 26{,}863 = 2.69 \times 10^4$ lb additional fuel was needed.

158. $\dfrac{10^{-8} \text{ g}}{\text{L}} \times \dfrac{1 \text{ lb}}{453.59 \text{ g}} \times \dfrac{1 \text{ L}}{1.0567 \text{ qt}} \times \dfrac{4 \text{ qt}}{1 \text{ gal}} = 8 \times 10^{-11}$ lb/gal

CHAPTER 3

Matter

2.   intermolecular forces

4.   liquids

6.   gaseous

8.   The *stronger* the inter-particle forces, the more rigid is the sample overall.

10.   Gases are easily compressed into smaller volumes, whereas solids and liquids are not. Because a gaseous sample consists mostly of empty space, it is this empty space that is compressed when pressure is applied to a gas.

12.   This is a chemical property: the red liquid bromine disappears and is replaced by a white solid.

14.   Magnesium is malleable and ductile.

16.   c

18.
- a.   physical; the iron is only being heated.
- b.   chemical; the sugars in the marshmallow are being reduced to carbon.
- c.   chemical; most strips contain a peroxide which decomposes.
- d.   chemical; the bleach oxidizes dyes in the fabric.
- e.   physical; evaporation is only a change of state.
- f   physical; the salt is only modifying the physical properties of the solution, not undergoing a chemical reaction.
- g.   chemical; the drain cleaner breaks bonds in the hair.
- h.   physical; students will most likely reply that this is a physical change since the perfume is evaporating; the sensation of smell, however, depends on chemical processes.
- i.   physical; the sublimation is only a change of state.
- j.   physical; the wood is only being physically divided into smaller pieces.
- k.   chemical; the cellulose in the wood is reacting with oxygen gas

20.   Compounds consist of two or more elements combined together chemically in a fixed composition, no matter what their source may be. For example, water on earth consists of molecules containing one oxygen atom and two hydrogen atoms. Water on Mars (or any other planet) has the same composition.

22.   compounds

24.   Typically, the properties of a compound and the elements that constitute it are very different. Consider the properties of liquid *water* and the hydrogen and oxygen gases from which the water was prepared. Consider the properties of *sodium chloride* (table salt) and the sodium metal and chlorine gas from which it might have been prepared.

26.   Given that the product of the process is no longer attracted by the magnet, this strongly suggests that the iron has been converted to an iron/sulfur compound—a pure substance.

28.   solutions: window cleaner, shampoo, rubbing alcohol

mixtures: salad dressing, jelly beans, the change in my pocket

30.   a.   primarily a pure compound   c.   mixture

b.   mixture   d.   pure substance

32.   Concrete is a mixture: the various components of the particular concrete are still distinguishable within the concrete if examined closely.

34.   Consider a mixture of salt (sodium chloride) and sand. Salt is soluble in water, sand is not. The mixture is added to water and stirred to dissolve the salt and is then filtered. The salt solution passes through the filter; the sand remains on the filter. The water can then be evaporated from the salt.

36.   The chemical identities of the components of the mixture are not changed by filtration or distillation: the various components are separated by physical, not chemical, means.

38.   Since X is a pure substance, the fact that two different solids form when electrical current is passed indicates that X must be a compound.

40.   Because vaporized water is still the *same substance* as solid water, no chemical reaction has occurred. Sublimation is a physical change.

42.   far apart

44.   chemical

46.   physical

48.   electrolysis

50.   a.   heterogeneous

b.   heterogeneous

c.   heterogeneous (unless you work hard to get all the lumps out!)

d.   although strictly heterogeneous, it may appear homogeneous

e.   heterogeneous

52.   Answer depends on student response

54.   physical, chemical

56. O_2 and P_4 are both still elements, even though the ordinary forms of these elements consist of molecules containing more than one atom (but all atoms in each respective molecule are the same). P_2O_5 is a compound, because it is made up of two or more different elements (not all the atoms in the P_2O_5 molecule are the same).

58.   Assuming there is enough water present in the mixture to have dissolved all the salt, filter the mixture to separate out the sand from the mixture. Then distill the filtrate (consisting of salt and water), which will boil off the water, leaving the salt.

60.   The most obvious difference is the physical states: water is a liquid under room conditions, hydrogen and oxygen are both gases. Hydrogen is flammable. Oxygen supports combustion. Water does neither.

CUMULATIVE REVIEW

Chapters 1–3

2.   By now, after having covered three chapters in this book, it is hoped that you have adopted an "active" approach to your study of chemistry. You may have discovered (perhaps through a disappointing grade on a quiz (though we hope not), that you really have to get involved with chemistry. You can't just sit and take notes, or just look over the solved examples in the textbook. You have to learn to solve problems. You have to learn how to interpret problems, and how to reduce them to the simple mathematical relationships you have studied. Whereas in some courses you might get by on just giving back on exams the facts or ideas presented in class, in chemistry you have to be able to extend and synthesize what has been discussed and to apply the material to new situations. Don't get discouraged if this is difficult at first: it's difficult for everyone at first.

4.   It is difficult sometimes for students (especially beginning students) to understand why certain subjects are required for a given college major. The faculty of your major department, however, have collectively many years of experience in the subject in which you have chosen to specialize. They really do know what courses will be helpful to you in the future. They may have had trouble with the same courses that now give you trouble, but they realize that all the work will be worth it in the end. Some courses you take, particularly in your major field itself, have obvious and immediate utility. Other courses, often times chemistry included, are provided to give you a general background knowledge, which may prove useful in understanding your own major or other subjects related to your major. In perhaps a burst of bravado, chemistry has been called "the central science" by one team of textbook authors. This moniker is very true however: in order to understand biology, physics, nutrition, farming, home economics, or whatever (it helps to have a general background in chemistry).

6.   Whenever a scientific measurement is made, we always employ the instrument or measuring device we are using to the limits of its precision. On a practical basis, this usually means that we *estimate* our reading of the last significant figure of the measurement. An example of the uncertainty in the last significant figure is given for measuring the length of a pin in the text in Figure 2.5. Scientists appreciate the limits of experimental techniques and instruments, and always assume that the last digit in a number representing a measurement has been estimated. Because the last significant figure in every measurement is assumed to be estimated, it is never possible to exclude uncertainty from measurements. The best we can do is to try to improve our techniques and instruments so that we get more significant figures for our measurements.

8.   Dimensional analysis is a method of problem solving that pays particular attention to the units of measurements and uses these units as if they were algebraic symbols that multiply, divide, and cancel. Consider the following example. A dozen eggs costs $1.25. Suppose we want to know how much one egg costs, and also how much three dozens of eggs will cost. To solve these problems, we need to make use of two equivalence statements:

> 1 dozen eggs = 12 eggs
>
> 1 dozen eggs = $1.25

The first of these equivalence statements is obvious: everyone knows that 12 eggs is "equivalent" to one dozen. The second statement also expresses an equivalence: if you give the grocer $1.25, he or she will give you a dozen eggs. From these equivalence statements, we can construct the conversion factors we need to answer the two questions. For the first question (what does one egg cost) we can set up the calculation as follows

$$\frac{\$1.25}{12 \text{ eggs}} = \$0.104 = \$0.10$$

as the cost of one egg. Similarly, for the second question (the cost of 3 dozens eggs), we can set up the conversion as follows

$$3 \text{ dozens} \times \frac{\$1.25}{1 \text{ dozen}} = \$3.75$$

as the cost of three dozens eggs. See Section 2.6 of the text for how we construct conversion factors from equivalence statements.

10. Defining what scientists mean by "matter" often seems circular to students. Scientists say that matter is something that "has mass and occupies space", without ever really explaining what it means to "have mass" or to "occupy space"! The concept of matter is so basic and fundamental, that it becomes difficult to give a good textbook definition other than to say that matter is the "stuff" of which everything is made. Matter can be classified and subdivided in many ways, depending on what we are trying to demonstrate.

On the most fundamental basis, all matter is composed of tiny particles (such as protons, electrons, neutrons, and the other subatomic particles). On one higher level, these tiny particles are combined in a systematic manner into units called atoms. Atoms, in turn, may be combined to constitute molecules. And finally, large groups of molecules may be placed together to form a bulk sample of substance that we can see.

Matter can also be classified as to the physical state a particular substance happens to take. Some substances are solids, some are liquids, and some are gases. Matter can also be classified as to whether it is a pure substance (one type of molecule) or a mixture (more than one type of molecule), and furthermore whether a mixture is homogeneous or heterogeneous.

12. Chemists tend to give a functional definition of what they mean by an "element": an element is a fundamental substance that cannot be broken down into any simpler substances by chemical methods. Compounds, on the other hand, can be broken down into simpler substances (the elements of which the compound is composed). For example, sulfur and oxygen are both elements (sulfur occurs as S_8 molecules and oxygen as O_2 molecules). When sulfur and oxygen are placed together and heated, the compound sulfur dioxide (SO_2) forms. When we analyze the sulfur dioxide produced, we notice that each and every molecule consists of one sulfur atom and two oxygen atoms, and on a mass basis, consists of 50% each of sulfur and oxygen. We describe this by saying that sulfur dioxide has a constant composition. The fact that a given compound has constant composition is usually expressed in terms of the mass percentages of the elements present in the compound. The reason the mass percentages are constant is because of a constant number of atoms of each type present in the compound's molecules. If a scientist anywhere in the universe analyzed sulfur dioxide, he or she would find the same composition: if a scientist finds something that does not have the same composition, then the substance cannot be sulfur dioxide.

14. a. The decimal point must be moved four places to the right: 8.917×10^{-4}

b. The decimal point must be moved four places to the left: 0.0002795

c. The decimal point must be moved three places to the right: 4913

     d.   The decimal point must be moved seven places to the left: 8.51×10^7

     e.   The arithmetic must be performed and then the exponents combined: 1.219×10^2

     f.   The arithmetic must be performed and then the exponents combined: 3.396×10^{-9}

16.   a.   two (based on the factor of 2.1 in the denominator)

     b.   two (based on the factor of 5.2 in the numerator)

     c.   three (one before the decimal point, and two after the decimal point)

     d.   three (based on the sum of 5.338 and 2.11)

     e.   one (based on 9 only having one significant figure)

     f.   two (based on the sum of 4.2005 and 2.7)

     g.   two (based on the factor of 0.15)

     h.   three (two before the decimal point, and one after the decimal point)

18.   density = mass/volume   mass = volume × density   volume = mass/density

     a. $\text{density} = \dfrac{78.5 \text{ g}}{100. \text{ mL}} = 0.785 \text{ g/mL}$

     b. $\text{volume} = \text{mass/density} = \dfrac{1.590 \text{ kg} \times \dfrac{1000 \text{ g}}{1 \text{ kg}}}{0.785 \text{ g/mL}} = 2025 \text{ mL} = 2.03 \text{ L}$

     c. $\text{mass} = \text{volume} \times \text{density} = 1.35 \text{ L} \times \dfrac{1000 \text{ mL}}{1 \text{ L}} \times \dfrac{0.785 \text{ g}}{1 \text{ mL}} = 1060 \text{ g} = 1.06 \text{ kg}$

     d. $\text{volume} = \text{mass/density} = \dfrac{25.2 \text{ g}}{2.70 \text{ g/cm}^3} = 9.33 \text{ cm}^3$

     e.   volume = 12.0 cm × 2.5 cm × 2.5 cm = 75 cm^3

                mass = volume × density = 75 cm^3 × 2.70 g/cm^3 = 202.5 g = 2.0×10^2 g

CHAPTER 4

Chemical Foundations: Elements, Atoms, and Ions

2.   Robert Boyle

4.   There are over 116 elements presently known; of these 88 occur naturally and the remaining are manmade. Table 4.1 lists the most common elements on the Earth.

6.   a.   Trace elements are those elements which are present in only tiny amounts in the body, but are critical for many bodily processes and functions.

        b.   Answer depends on your choice of elements

8.   Sometimes the symbol for an element is based on its common name in another language. This is true for many of the more common metals since their existence was known to the ancients: some examples are iron, sodium, potassium, silver, and tin (the symbols come from their name in Latin); tungsten (the symbol comes from its name in German).

10.   a.   9

        b.   6

        c.   8

        d.   12

        e.   11

        f.   13

        g.   3

        h.   5

        i.   4

        j.   2

12.   Zr   zirconium

        Cs   cesium

        Se   selenium

        Au   gold

        Ce   cerium

14.   B: barium, Ba; berkelium, Bk; beryllium, Be; bismuth, Bi; bohrium, Bh; boron, B; bromine, Br

        N: neodymium, Nd; neon, Ne; neptunium, Np; nickel, Ni; niobium, Nb; nitrogen, N; nobelium, No

P: palladium, Pd; phosphorus, P; platinum, Pt; plutonium, Pu; polonium, Po; potassium, K; praseodymium, Pr; promethium, Pm; protactinium, Pa

S: samarium, Sm; scandium, Sc; seaborgium, Sg; selenium, Se; silicon, Si; silver, Ag; sodium, Na; strontium, Sr; sulfur, S

16. a.   Elements are made of tiny particles called atoms.

   b.   All the atoms of a given element are identical

   c.   The atoms of a given element are different from those of any other element.

   d.   A given compound always has the same numbers and types of atoms.

   e.   Atoms are neither created nor destroyed in chemical processes. A chemical reaction simply changes the way the atoms are grouped together.

18.   According to Dalton, all atoms of the same element are *identical*; in particular, every atom of a given element has the same *mass* as every other atom of that element. If a given compound always contains the *same relative numbers* of atoms of each kind, and those atoms always have the *same masses*, then it follows that the compound made from those elements would always contain the same relative masses of its elements.

20. a. CO_2 d. H_2SO_4

   b. CO e. $BaCl_2$

   c. $CaCO_3$ f. Al_2S_3

22. a.   False; Rutherford's bombardment experiments with metal foil suggested that the alpha particles were being deflected by coming near a *dense, positively charged* atomic nucleus.

   b.   False; The proton and the electron have opposite charges, but the mass of the electron is *much smaller* than the mass of the proton.

   c.   True

24.   The protons and neutrons are found in the nucleus. The protons are positively charged; the neutrons have no electrical charge. Protons and neutrons each have approximately the same mass.

26.   neutron; electron

28.   Because they are located in the exterior regions of the atom, it is the electrons of an atom that most interact with other atoms and are therefore most responsible for the atom's chemical behavior.

30.   The atomic number represents the number of protons in the nucleus of the atom, and makes the atom a particular element. The mass number represents the total number of protons and neutrons in the nucleus of an atom, and distinguishes one isotope of an element from another.

32.   Neutrons are uncharged and contribute only to the mass.

34.   Atoms of the same element (i.e., atoms with the same number of protons in the nucleus) may have different numbers of neutrons, and so will have different masses.

36.

Z	Symbol	Name
14	Si	silicon
54	Xe	xenon
79	Au	gold
56	Ba	barium
53	I	iodine
50	Sn	tin
48	Cd	cadmium

38. a. $^{54}_{26}\text{Fe}$

   b. $^{56}_{26}\text{Fe}$

   c. $^{57}_{26}\text{Fe}$

   d. $^{14}_{7}\text{N}$

   e. $^{15}_{7}\text{N}$

   f. $^{15}_{7}\text{N}$

40. The relative amounts of ^2H and ^{18}O in a person's hair, compared to other isotopes of these elements, vary significantly from region to region in the United States and is related to the isotopic abundances in the drinking water in a region.

42.

Name	Symbol	Atomic Number	Mass Number	Number of neutrons
oxygen	$^{17}_{8}\text{O}$	8	17	9
oxygen	$^{17}_{8}\text{O}$	8	17	9
Neon	$^{20}_{10}\text{Ne}$	10	20	10
iron	$^{56}_{26}\text{Fe}$	26	56	30
plutonium	$^{244}_{94}\text{Pu}$	94	244	150
mercury	$^{202}_{80}\text{Hg}$	80	202	122
cobalt	$^{59}_{27}\text{Co}$	27	59	32
nickel	$^{56}_{28}\text{Ni}$	28	56	28
fluorine	$^{19}_{9}\text{F}$	9	19	10
chromium	$^{50}_{24}\text{Cr}$	24	50	26

44. Elements with similar chemical properties are aligned *vertically* in families known as *groups*.

46. Metallic elements are found towards the *left* and *bottom* of the periodic table; there are far more metallic elements than there are nonmetals.

48. The gaseous nonmetallic elements are hydrogen, nitrogen, oxygen, fluorine, chlorine, plus all the group 8 elements (noble gases). There are no gaseous metallic elements under room conditions.

50.   The metalloids are the elements found on either side of the "stairstep" region that is marked on most periodic tables. The metalloid elements show some properties of both metals and nonmetals.

52.   a.   fluorine, chlorine, bromine, iodine, astatine

        b.   lithium, sodium, potassium, rubidium, cesium, francium

        c.   beryllium, magnesium, calcium, strontium, barium, radium

        d.   helium, neon, argon, krypton, xenon, radon

54.   Arsenic, atomic number 33, is located on the dividing line between the metallic elements and the non-metallic elements, and is therefore classified as a metalloid. Arsenic is in Group 5 of the periodic table, whose other principal members are N, P, Sb, and Bi.

56.   Most of the elements are too reactive to be found in the uncombined form in nature and are found only in compounds.

58.   These elements are found *uncombined* in nature and do not readily react with other elements. For many years it was thought that these elements formed no compounds at all, although this has now been shown to be untrue.

60.   diatomic gases: H_2, N_2, O_2, Cl_2, and F_2

        monatomic gases: He, Ne, Kr, Xe, Rn, and Ar

62.   chlorine

64.   diamond

66.   electrons

68.   3+

70.   *-ide*

72.   nonmetallic

74.   a.   36   d.   36

        b.   36   e.   80

        c.   21   f.   27

76.   a.   two electrons gained

        b.   three electrons gained

        c.   three electrons lost

        d.   two electrons lost

        e.   one electron lost

        f.   two electrons lost.

78. a. P^{3-}

b. Ra^{2+}

c. At^-

d.   no ion

e. Cs^+

f. Se^{2-}

80.   Sodium chloride is an *ionic* compound, consisting of Na^+ and Cl^- *ions*. When NaCl is dissolved in water, these ions are *set free*, and can move independently to conduct the electrical current. Sugar crystals, although they may visually *appear* similar contain *no* ions. When sugar is dissolved in water, it dissolves as uncharged *molecules*. There are no electrically charged species present in a sugar solution to carry the electrical current.

82.   The total number of positive charges must equal the total number of negative charges so that there will be *no net charge* on the crystals of an ionic compound. A macroscopic sample of compound must ordinarily not have any net charge.

84. a. CsI, BaI_2, AlI_3

b. Cs_2O, BaO, Al_2O_3

c. Cs_3P, Ba_3P_2, AlP

d. $Cs_2Se, BaSe, Al_2Se_3$

e. CsH, BaH_2, AlH_3

86. a.   7; halogens

b.   8; noble gases

c.   2; alkaline earth elements

d.   2; alkaline earth elements

e.   4

f.   6; (the members of group 6 are sometimes called the chalcogens)

g.   8; noble gases

h.   1; alkali metals

88.

	Element	Symbol	Atomic Number
Group 3	boron	B	5
	aluminum	Al	13
	gallium	Ga	31
	indium	In	49
Group 5	nitrogen	N	7
	phosphorus	P	15
	arsenic	As	33
	antimony	Sb	51

Group 6	oxygen	O	8
	sulfur	S	16
	selenium	Se	34
	tellurium	Te	52
Group 8	helium	He	2
	neon	Ne	10
	argon	Ar	18
	krypton	Kr	36

90.   Most of the mass of an atom is concentrated in the nucleus: the *protons* and *neutrons* that constitute the nucleus have similar masses, and these particles are nearly two thousand times heavier than electrons. The chemical properties of an atom depend on the number and location of the *electrons* it possesses. Electrons are found in the outer regions of the atom and are the particles most likely to be involved in interactions between atoms.

92. $C_6H_{12}O_6$

94.   a.   29 protons; 34 neutrons; 29 electrons

       b.   35 protons; 45 neutrons; 35 electrons

       c.   12 protons; 12 neutrons; 12 electrons

96.   The chief use of gold in ancient times was as *ornamentation*, whether in statuary or in jewelry. Gold possesses an especially beautiful luster, and because it is relatively soft and malleable, it could be worked finely by artisans. Among the metals, gold is particularly inert to attack by most substances in the environment.

98.   a.   I

       b.   Si

       c.   W

       d.   Fe

       e.   Cu

       f.   Co

100.   a.   Br

       b.   Bi

       c.   Hg

       d.   V

       e.   F

       f.   Ca

102.   a.   osmium

       b.   zirconium

       c.   rubidium

       d.   radon

e.   uranium

f.   manganese

g.   nickel

h.   bromine

104.   a. CO_2

b. $AlCl_3$

c. $HClO_4$

d. SCl_6

106.   a. $^{13}_{6}C$

b. $^{13}_{6}C$

c. $^{13}_{6}C$

d. $^{44}_{19}K$

e. $^{41}_{20}Ca$

f. $^{35}_{19}K$

108.

Symbol	Protons	Neutrons	Mass Number
$^{41}_{20}Ca$	20	21	41
$^{55}_{25}Mn$	25	30	55
$^{109}_{47}Ag$	47	62	109
$^{45}_{21}Sc$	21	24	45

CHAPTER 5

Nomenclature

2. A binary compound contains only two elements: the major types of binary compounds are *ionic* (compounds that contain a metal and a nonmetal) and *nonionic* (compounds containing two nonmetals).

4. cation

6. Some substances do not contain molecules. For example, the substance sodium chloride consists of an extended lattice array of sodium ions, Na^+, and chloride ions, Cl^-. Each sodium ion is surrounded by several chloride ions, and each chloride ion is surrounded by several sodium ions. We write the formula as NaCl to indicate the relative number of each ion in the substance, not to indicate that there are "molecules" of sodium chloride.

8. Roman numeral

10. a. lithium chloride

    b. barium fluoride

    c. calcium oxide

    d. aluminum iodide

    e. magnesium sulfide

    f. rubidium oxide

12. a. correct

    b. incorrect; copper(I) oxide

    c. incorrect; potassium oxide

    d. correct

    e. incorrect; rubidium sulfide

14. a. As the chloride ion has a 1– charge, the copper ion must have a 2+ charge: the name is copper(II) chloride.

    b. As the oxide ion has a 2– charge, the chromium ion must have a 3+ charge: the name is chromium(III) oxide.

    c. As the chloride ion has a 1– charge, the mercury ion must have a 2+ charge: the name is mercury(II) chloride.

    d. As the oxide ion has a 2– charge, each mercury ion must have a 1+ charge: the name is mercury(I) oxide.

    e. As the bromide ion has a 1– charge, the gold ion must have a 3+ charge: the name is gold(III) bromide.

   f.   As the oxide ion has a 2– charge, the manganese ion must have a 4+ charge: the name is manganese(IV) oxide.

16.   a.   As each chloride ion has a 1– charge, the cobalt ion must have a 3+ charge: the name is cobalt*ic* chloride.

   b.   As each bromide ion has a 1– charge, the iron ion must have a 2+ charge: the name is fer*rous* bromide.

   c.   As each oxide ion has a 2– charge, the lead ion must have a 4+ charge: the name is plumb*ic* oxide.

   d.   As each chloride ion has a 1– charge, the tin ion must have a 4+ charge: the name is stann*ic* chloride.

   e.   As the iodide ion has a 1– charge, the mercury ion must have a 2+ charge: the name is mercur*ic* iodide.

   f.   As the sulfide ion has a 2– charge, the iron ion must have a 2+ charge: the name is fer*rous* sulfide.

18.   Remember that for this type of compound of nonmetals, numerical prefixes are used to indicate how many of each type of atom are present. However, if only one atom of the first element mentioned in the compound is present in a molecule, the prefix *mono–* is not needed.

   a.   chlorine pentafluoride

   b.   xenon dichloride

   c.   selenium dioxide

   d.   dinitrogen trioxide

   e.   diiodine hexachloride

   f.   carbon disulfide

20.   a.   lead(IV) sulfide, plumbic sulfide – ionic

   b.   lead(II) sulfide, plumbous sulfide – ionic

   c.   silicon dioxide – nonionic

   d.   tin(IV) fluoride, stannic fluoride – ionic

   e.   dichlorine heptoxide – nonionic

   f.   cobalt(III) sulfide, cobaltic sulfide – ionic

22.   a.   barium fluoride – ionic

   b.   radium oxide – ionic

   c.   dinitrogen oxide – nonionic

   d.   rubidium oxide – ionic

   e.   diarsenic pentoxide – nonionic

   f.   calcium nitride – ionic

24. An oxyanion is a polyatomic ion containing a given element and one or more oxygen atoms. The oxyanions of chlorine and bromine are given below:

Oxyanion	Name	Oxyanion	Name
ClO^-	hypochlorite	BrO^-	hypobromite
ClO_2^-	chlorite	BrO_2^-	bromite
ClO_3^-	chlorate	BrO_3^-	bromate
ClO_4^-	perchlorate	BrO_4^-	perbromate

26. For a series of oxyanions, the prefix *hypo–* is used for the anion with the fewest oxygen atoms, and the prefix *per–* is used for the anion with the most oxygen atoms.

28. IO^- hypoiodite

      IO_2^- iodite

      IO_3^- iodate

      IO_4^- periodate

30. a. NO_3^-

    b. NO_2^-

    c. NH_4^+

    d. CN^-

32. CN^- cyanide

      CO_3^{2-} carbonate

      HCO_3^- hydrogen carbonate

      $C_2H_3O_2^-$ acetate

34. a.   ammonium

    b.   dihydrogen phosphate

    c.   sulfate

    d.   hydrogen sulfite (also called *bi*sulfite)

    e.   perchlorate

    f.   iodate

36. a.   sodium permanganate

    b.   aluminum phosphate

    c.   chromium(II) carbonate, chromous carbonate

    d.   calcium hypochlorite

    e.   barium carbonate

    f.   calcium chromate

38. oxygen (commonly referred to as *oxy*acids)

40. a. hypochlorous acid

b. sulfurous acid

c. bromic acid

d. hypoiodous acid

e. perbromic acid

f. hydrosulfuric acid

g. hydroselenic acid

h. phosphorous acid

42. a. MgF_2

b. FeI_3

c. HgS

d. Ba_3N_2

e. $PbCl_2$

f. SnF_4

g. Ag_2O

h. K_2Se

44. a. N_2O

b. NO_2

c. N_2O_4

d. SF_6

e. PBr_3

f. CI_4

g. OCl_2

46. a. $NH_4C_2H_3O_2$

b. $Fe(OH)_2$

c. $Co_2(CO_3)_3$

d. $BaCr_2O_7$

e. $PbSO_4$

f. KH_2PO_4

g. Li_2O_2

h. $Zn(ClO_3)_2$

48. a. HCN

b. HNO_3

c. H_2SO_4

d. H_3PO_4

e.   HClO or HOCl

f.   HBr

g. $HBrO_2$

h.   HF

50. a. $Ca(HSO_4)_2$

b. $Zn_3(PO_4)_2$

c. $Fe(ClO_4)_3$

d. $Co(OH)_3$

e. K_2CrO_4

f. $Al(H_2PO_4)_3$

g. $LiHCO_3$

h. $Mn(C_2H_3O_2)_2$

i. $MgHPO_4$

j. $CsClO_2$

k. BaO_2

l. $NiCO_3$

52. A moist paste of NaCl would contain Na^+ and Cl^- ions in solution, and would serve as a *conductor* of electrical impulses.

54. $H \rightarrow H^+$ (hydrogen ion: a cation) $+ e^-$

$H + e^- \rightarrow H^-$ (hydr*ide* ion: an anion)

56. missing oxyanions: IO_3^-; ClO_2^-

missing oxyacids: $HClO_4$; HClO; $HBrO_2$

58. a.   gold(III) bromide, auric bromide

b.   cobalt(III) cyanide, cobaltic cyanide

c.   magnesium hydrogen phosphate

d.   diboron hexahydride (diborane is its common name)

e.   ammonia

f.   silver(I) sulfate (usually called silver sulfate)

g.   beryllium hydroxide

60. a.   ammonium carbonate

b.   ammonium hydrogen carbonate, ammonium bicarbonate

     c.   calcium phosphate

     d.   sulfurous acid

     e.   manganese(IV) oxide

     f.   iodic acid

     g.   potassium hydride

62.   a. $M(C_2H_3O_2)_4$

     b. $M(MnO_4)_4$

     c. MO_2

     d. $M(HPO_4)_2$

     e. $M(OH)_4$

     f. $M(NO_2)_4$

64. M^+ compounds: MD, M_2E, M_3F

     M^{2+} compounds: MD_2, ME, M_3F_2

     M^{3+} compounds: MD_3, M_2E_3, MF

66.

$Ca(NO_3)_2$	$CaSO_4$	$Ca(HSO_4)_2$	$Ca(H_2PO_4)_2$	CaO	$CaCl_2$
$Sr(NO_3)_2$	$SrSO_4$	$Sr(HSO_4)_2$	$Sr(H_2PO_4)_2$	SrO	$SrCl_2$
NH_4NO_3	$(NH_4)_2SO_4$	NH_4HSO_4	$NH_4H_2PO_4$	$(NH_4)_2O$	NH_4Cl
$Al(NO_3)_3$	$Al_2(SO_4)_3$	$Al(HSO_4)_3$	$Al(H_2PO_4)_3$	Al_2O_3	$AlCl_3$
$Fe(NO_3)_3$	$Fe_2(SO_4)_3$	$Fe(HSO_4)_3$	$Fe(H_2PO_4)_3$	Fe_2O_3	$FeCl_3$
$Ni(NO_3)_2$	$NiSO_4$	$Ni(HSO_4)_2$	$Ni(H_2PO_4)_2$	NiO	$NiCl_2$
$AgNO_3$	Ag_2SO_4	$AgHSO_4$	AgH_2PO_4	Ag_2O	$AgCl$
$Au(NO_3)_3$	$Au_2(SO_4)_3$	$Au(HSO_4)_3$	$Au(H_2PO_4)_3$	Au_2O_3	$AuCl_3$
KNO_3	K_2SO_4	$KHSO_4$	KH_2PO_4	K_2O	KCl
$Hg(NO_3)_2$	$HgSO_4$	$Hg(HSO_4)_2$	$Hg(H_2PO_4)_2$	HgO	$HgCl_2$
$Ba(NO_3)_2$	$BaSO_4$	$Ba(HSO_4)_2$	$Ba(H_2PO_4)_2$	BaO	$BaCl_2$

68.   helium

70.   iodine (solid), bromine (liquid), fluorine and chlorine (gases)

72.   1−

74.   1−

76.   a. $Al(13e^-) \rightarrow Al^{3+}(10e^-) + 3e^-$

     b. $S(16e^-) + 2e^- \rightarrow S^{2-}(18e^-)$

     c. $Cu(29e^-) \rightarrow Cu^+(28e^-) + e^-$

     d. $F(9e^-) + e^- \rightarrow F^-(10e^-)$

     e. $Zn(30e^-) \rightarrow Zn^{2+}(28e^-) + 2e^-$

     f. $P(15e^-) + 3e^- \rightarrow P^{3-}(18e^-)$

78.   a.   Two 1+ ions are needed to balance a 2– ion, so the formula must have two Na^+ ions for each S^{2-} ion: Na_2S.

       b.   One 1+ ion exactly balances a 1– ion, so the formula should have an equal number of K^+ and Cl^- ions: KCl.

       c.   One 2+ ion exactly balances a 2– ion, so the formula must have an equal number of Ba^{2+} and O^{2-} ions: BaO.

       d.   One 2+ ion exactly balances a 2– ion, so the formula must have an equal number of Mg^{2+} and Se^{2-} ions: $MgSe$.

       e.   One 2+ ion requires two 1– ions to balance charge, so the formula must have twice as many Br^- ions as Cu^{2+} ions: $CuBr_2$.

       f.   One 3+ ion requires three 1– ions to balance charge, so the formula must have three times as many I^- ions as Al^{3+} ions: AlI_3.

       g.   Two 3+ ions give a total of 6+, whereas three 2– ions will give a total of 6–. The formula then should contain two Al^{3+} ions and three O^{2-} ions: Al_2O_3.

       h.   Three 2+ ions are required to balance two 3– ions, so the formula must contain three Ca^{2+} ions for every two N^{3-} ions: Ca_3N_2.

80.   a.   silver(I) oxide or just silver oxide

       b.   correct

       c.   iron(III) oxide

       d.   plumbic oxide

       e.   correct

82.   a.   stannous chloride

       b.   ferrous oxide

       c.   stannic oxide

       d.   plumbous sulfide

       e.   cobaltic sulfide

       f.   chromous chloride

84.   a.   iron(III) acetate, ferric acetate

       b.   bromine monofluoride

       c.   potassium peroxide

       d.   silicon tetrabromide

       e.   copper(II) permanganate, cupric permanganate

       f.   calcium chromate

86.   a. CO_3^{2-}

       b. HCO_3^-

     c. $C_2H_3O_2^-$

     d. CN^-

88.   a.   carbonate

     b.   chlorate

     c.   sulfate

     d.   phosphate

     e.   perchlorate

     f.   permanganate

90.   Answer depends on student choices.

92.   a. NaH_2PO_4

     b. $LiClO_4$

     c. $Cu(HCO_3)_2$

     d. $KC_2H_3O_2$

     e. BaO_2

     f. Cs_2SO_3

Chapters 4 and 5

2.   How many elements could you name? Although you certainly don't have to memorize all the
      elements, you should at least be able to give the symbol or name for the most common elements
      (listed in Table 4.3).

4.   Dalton's atomic theory as presented in this text consists of five main postulates. Although
      Dalton's theory was exceptional scientific thinking for its time, some of the postulates have been
      modified as our scientific instruments and calculation methods have become increasingly more
      sophisticated. The main postulates of Dalton's theory are as follows: (1) Elements are made up of
      tiny particles called atoms; (2) all atoms of a given element are identical; (3) although all atoms
      of a given element are identical, these atoms are different from the atoms of all other elements;
      (4) atoms of one element can combine with atoms of another element to form a compound, and
      such a compound will always have the same relative numbers and types of atoms for its
      composition; and (5) atoms are merely rearranged into new groupings during an ordinary
      chemical reaction, and no atom is ever destroyed and no new atom is ever created during such a
      reaction.

6.   The expression *nuclear* atom indicates that we view the atom as having a dense center of positive
      charge (called the nucleus) around which the electrons move through primarily empty space.
      Rutherford's experiment involved shooting a beam of particles at a thin sheet of metal foil.
      According to the then current "plum pudding" model of the atom, most of these positively-
      charged particles should have passed right through the foil. However, Rutherford detected that a
      significant number of particles effectively bounced off something and were deflected backwards
      to the source of particles, and that other particles were deflected from the foil at large angles.
      Rutherford realized that his observations could be explained if the atoms of the metal foil had a
      small, dense, positively-charged nucleus, with a significant amount of empty space between
      nuclei. The empty space between nuclei would allow most of the particles to pass through the
      atom. However, if a particle hit a nucleus head-on, it would be deflected backwards at the source.
      If a positively-charged particle passed near a positively-charged nucleus (but did not hit the
      nucleus head-on), then the particle would be deflected by the repulsive forces between the
      positive charges. Rutherford's experiment conclusively disproved the "plum pudding" model for
      the atom, which envisioned the atom as a uniform sphere of positive charge, with enough
      negatively-charged electrons scattered through the atom to balance out the positive charge.

8.   Isotopes represent atoms of the same element which have different atomic masses. Isotopes are a
      result of the fact that atoms of a given element may have different numbers of neutrons in their
      nuclei. Isotopes have the same atomic number (number of protons in the nucleus) but have
      different mass numbers (total number of protons and neutrons in the nucleus). The different
      isotopes of an atom are indicated by symbolism of the form $_Z^A X$ in which Z represents the atomic
      number, and A the mass number, of element X. For example, $_6^{13}C$ represents a nuclide of carbon
      with atomic number 6 (6 protons in the nucleus) and mass number 13 (reflecting 6 protons plus 7
      neutrons in the nucleus). The various isotopes of an element have identical chemical properties
      because the chemical properties of an atom are a function of the electrons in the atom (*not* the

nucleus). The physical properties of the isotopes of an element (and compounds containing those isotopes) may differ because of the difference in mass of the isotopes.

10.   Most elements are too reactive to be found in nature in other than the combined form. Aside from the noble metals gold, silver, and platinum, the only other elements commonly found in nature in the uncombined state are some of the gaseous elements (such as O2, N2, He, Ar, etc.), and the solid nonmetals carbon and sulfur.

12.   Ionic compounds typically are hard, crystalline solids with high melting and boiling points. Ionic substances like sodium chloride, when dissolved in water or when melted, conduct electrical currents: chemists have taken this evidence to mean that ionic substances consist of positively– and negatively–charged particles (ions). Although an ionic substance is made up of positively– and negatively–charged particles, there is no net electrical charge on a sample of such a substance because the total number of positive charges is balanced by an equal number of negative charges. An ionic compound could not possibly exist of just cations or just anions: there must be a balance of charge or the compound would be very unstable (like charges repel each other).

14.   When naming ionic compounds, we name the positive ion (cation) first. For simple binary Type I ionic compounds, the ending –ide is added to the root name of the element that is the negative ion (anion). For example, for the Type I ionic compound formed between potassium and sulfur, K_2S, the name would be potassium sulfide: potassium is the cation, sulfur is the anion (with the suffix –ide added). Type II compounds are named by either of two systems, the "ous–ic" system (which is falling out of use), and the "Roman numeral" system which is preferred by most chemists. Type II compounds involve elements that form more than one stable ion. It is therefore necessary to specify which ion is present in a given compound. For example, iron forms two types of stable ion: Fe^{2+} and Fe^{3+}. Iron can react with oxygen to form either of two stable oxides, FeO or Fe_2O_3, depending on which cation is involved. Under the Roman numeral naming system, FeO would be named iron(II) oxide to show that it contains Fe^{2+} ions; Fe_2O_3 would be named iron(III) oxide to indicate that it contains Fe^{3+} ions. The Roman numeral used in a name corresponds to the charge of the specific ion present in the compound. Under the less-favored "ous–ic" system, for an element that forms two stable ions, the ending –ous is used to indicate the lower-charged ion, whereas the ending –ic is used to indicate the higher-charged ion. FeO and Fe_2O_3 would thus be named ferrous oxide and ferric oxide, respectively. The "ous–ic" system has fallen out of favor because it does not indicate the actual charge on the ion, but only that it is the lower or higher charged of the two. This can lead to confusion: for example Fe^{2+} is called ferrous ion in this system, but Cu^{2+} is called cupric ion (since there is also a Cu^+ stable ion).

16.   A polyatomic ion is an ion containing more than one atom. Some common polyatomic ions you should be familiar with are listed in Table 5.4. Parentheses are used in writing formulas containing polyatomic ions to indicate unambiguously how many of the polyatomic ion are present in the formula, to make certain that there is no mistake as to what is meant by the formula. For example, consider the substance calcium phosphate. The correct formula for this substance is $Ca_3(PO_4)_2$, which indicates that three calcium ions are combined for every two phosphate ions (check the total number of positive and negative charges to see why this is so). If we did not write the parenthesis around the formula for the phosphate ion, that is, if we had written Ca_3PO_{42}, people reading this formula might think that there were 42 oxygen atoms present!

18.   Acids, in general, are substances that produce protons (H^+ ions) when dissolved in water. For acids that do not contain oxygen, the prefix hydro– and the suffix –ic are used with the root name of the element present in the acid (for example: HCl, hydrochloric acid; H_2S, hydrosulfuric acid;

HF, hydrofluoric acid). The nomenclature of acids whose anions contain oxygen is more complicated. A series of prefixes and suffixes is used with the name of the non-oxygen atom in the anion of the acid: these prefixes and suffixes indicate the relative (not actual) number of oxygen atoms present in the anion. Most of the elements that form oxyanions form two such anions: for example, sulfur forms sulfite ion (SO_3^{2-}) and sulfate ion (SO_4^{2-}), and nitrogen forms nitrite ion (NO_2^-) and nitrate ion (NO_3^-). For an element that forms two oxyanions, the acid containing the anions will have the ending –*ous* if the anion is the –*ite* anion and the ending –*ic* if the anion is the –*ate* anion. For example, HNO_2 is nitr*ous* acid and HNO_3 is nitr*ic* acid; H_2SO_3 is sulfur*ous* acid and H_2SO_4 is sulfur*ic* acid. The halogen elements (Group 7) each form four oxyanions, and consequently, four oxyacids. The prefix *hypo*– is used for the oxyacid that contains fewer oxygen atoms than the –*ite* anion, and the prefix *per*– is used for the oxyacid that contains more oxygen atoms than the –*ate* anion. For example,

Acid	*Name*	*Anion*	*Anion name*
HBrO	*hypo*brom*ous* acid	BrO^-	*hypo*brom*ite*
$HBrO_2$	brom*ous* acid	BrO_2^-	brom*ite*
$HBrO_3$	brom*ic* acid	BrO_3^-	brom*ate*
$HBrO_4$	*per*brom*ic* acid	BrO_4^-	*per*brom*ate*

20. How many elements in each family could you name? Elements in the same family have the same type of electronic configuration, and tend to undergo similar chemical reactions with other groups. For example, Li, Na, K, Rb, Cs all react with elemental chlorine gas, Cl_2, to form an ionic compound of general formula M^+Cl^-.

22. a. 8 electrons, 8 protons, 9 neutrons

   b. 92 electrons, 92 protons, 143 neutrons

   c. 17 electrons, 17 protons, 20 neutrons

   d. 1 electrons, 1 protons, 2 neutrons

   e. 2 electrons, 2 protons, 2 neutrons

   f. 50 electrons, 50 protons, 69 neutrons

   g. 54 electrons, 54 protons, 70 neutrons

   h. 30 electrons, 30 protons, 34 neutrons

24. a. 12 protons, 10 electrons

   b. 26 protons, 24 electrons

   c. 26 protons, 23 electrons

   d. 9 protons, 10 electrons

   e. 28 protons, 26 electrons

   f. 30 protons, 28 electrons

   g. 27 protons, 24 electrons

   h. 7 protons, 10 electrons

   i. 16 protons, 18 electrons

j.   37 protons, 36 electrons

k.   34 protons, 36 electrons

l.   19 protons, 18 electrons

26.   a.   CuI

        b. $CoCl_2$

        c. Ag_2S

        d. Hg_2Br_2

        e.   HgO

        f. Cr_2S_3

        g. PbO_2

        h. K_3N

        i. SnF_2

        j. Fe_2O_3

28.   a. NH_4^+, ammonium ion

        b. SO_3^{2-}, sulfite ion

        c. NO_3^-, nitrate ion

        d. SO_4^{2-}, sulfate ion

        e. NO_2^-, nitrite ion

        f. CN^-, cyanide ion

        g. OH^-, hydroxide ion

        h. ClO_4^-, perchlorate ion

        i. ClO^-, hypochlorite ion

        j. PO_4^{3-}, phosphate ion

30.   a.   xenon dioxide

        b.   iodine pentachloride

        c.   phosphorus trichloride

        d.   carbon monoxide

        e.   oxygen difluoride

        f.   diphosphorus pentoxide

        g.   arsenic triiodide

        h.   sulfur trioxide

CHAPTER 6

Chemical Reactions: An Introduction

2.   Most of these products contain a peroxide, which decomposes releasing oxygen gas.

4.   Bubbling takes place as the hydrogen peroxide chemically decomposes into water and oxygen gas.

6.   The appearance of the black color actually signals the breakdown of starches and sugars in the bread to elemental carbon. You may also see steam coming from the bread (water produced by the breakdown of the carbohydrates).

8.   atoms

10.   Balancing an equation ensures that no atoms are created or destroyed during the reaction. The total mass after the reaction must be the same as the total mass before the reaction.

12.   For solids we use (s), for liquids we use (l), and for gases we use (g).

14. $H_2O_2(aq) \rightarrow H_2(g) + O_2(g)$

16. $N_2H_4(l) \rightarrow N_2(g) + H_2(g)$

18. $C_3H_8(g) + O_2(g) \rightarrow CO_2(g) + H_2O(g)$

        $C_3H_8(g) + O_2(g) \rightarrow CO(g) + H_2O(g)$

20. $CaCO_3(s) + HCl(aq) \rightarrow CaCl_2(aq) + H_2O(l) + CO_2(g)$

22. $SiO_2(s) + C(s) \rightarrow Si(s) + CO(g)$

24. $Fe(s) + H_2O(g) \rightarrow FeO(s) + H_2(g)$

26. $SO_2(g) + H_2O(l) \rightarrow H_2SO_3(aq)$

        $SO_3(g) + H_2O(l) \rightarrow H_2SO_4(aq)$

28. $NO(g) + O_3(g) \rightarrow NO_2(g) + O_2(g)$

30. $P_4(s) + O_2(g) \rightarrow P_2O_5(s)$

32. $Xe(g) + F_2(g) \rightarrow XeF_4(s)$

34. $NH_3(g) + O_2(g) \rightarrow HNO_3(aq) + H_2O(l)$

36.   We cannot change the identities or formulas of the reactants or products in a chemical equation when balancing the equation. The proposed equation has incorrectly changed one of the products from water to hydrogen gas.

38.   a. $Zn(s) + CuO(s) \rightarrow ZnO(s) + Cu(l)$

The equation is already balanced.

b. $P_4(s) + F_2(g) \rightarrow PF_3(g)$

balance phosphorus: $P_4(s) + F_2(g) \rightarrow \mathbf{4}PF_3(g)$

balance fluorine: $P_4(s) + \mathbf{6F_2}(g) \rightarrow 4PF_3(g)$

balanced equation: $P_4(s) + 6F_2(g) \rightarrow 4PF_3(g)$

c. $Xe(g) + F_2(g) \rightarrow XeF_4(s)$

balance fluorine: $Xe(g) + \mathbf{2}F_2(g) \rightarrow XeF_4(s)$

balanced equation: $Xe(g) + 2F_2(g) \rightarrow XeF_4(s)$

d. $NH_4Cl(g) + Mg(OH)_2(s) \rightarrow NH_3(g) + H_2O(g) + MgCl_2(s)$

balance chlorine: $\mathbf{2}NH_4Cl(g) + Mg(OH)_2(s) \rightarrow NH_3(g) + H_2O(g) + MgCl_2(s)$

balance nitrogen: $2NH_4Cl(g) + Mg(OH)_2(s) \rightarrow \mathbf{2}NH_3(g) + H_2O(g) + MgCl_2(s)$

balance oxygen: $2NH_4Cl(g) + Mg(OH)_2(s) \rightarrow 2NH_3(g) + \mathbf{2}H_2O(g) + MgCl_2(s)$

balanced equation: $2NH_4Cl(g) + Mg(OH)_2(s) \rightarrow 2NH_3(g) + 2H_2O(g) + MgCl_2(s)$

e. $SiO(s) + Cl_2(g) \rightarrow SiCl_4(l) + O_2(g)$

balance oxygen: $\mathbf{2}SiO(s) + Cl_2(g) \rightarrow SiCl_4(l) + O_2(g)$

balanced silicon: $2SiO(s) + Cl_2(g) \rightarrow \mathbf{2}SiCl_4(l) + O_2(g)$

balance chlorine: $2SiO(s) + \mathbf{4}Cl_2(g) \rightarrow 2SiCl_4(l) + O_2(g)$

balanced equation: $2SiO(s) + 4Cl_2(g) \rightarrow 2SiCl_4(l) + O_2(g)$

f. $Cs_2O(s) + H_2O(l) \rightarrow CsOH(aq)$

balance cesium: $Cs_2O(s) + H_2O(l) \rightarrow \mathbf{2}CsOH(aq)$

balanced equation: $Cs_2O(s) + H_2O(l) \rightarrow 2CsOH(aq)$

g. $N_2O_3(g) + H_2O(l) \rightarrow HNO_2(aq)$

balance hydrogen: $N_2O_3(g) + H_2O(l) \rightarrow \mathbf{2}HNO_2(aq)$

balanced equation: $N_2O_3(g) + H_2O(l) \rightarrow 2HNO_2(aq)$

h. $Fe_2O_3(s) + H_2SO_4(l) \rightarrow Fe_2(SO_4)_3(s) + H_2O(g)$

balance sulfate ions: $Fe_2O_3(s) + \mathbf{3}H_2SO_4(l) \rightarrow Fe_2(SO_4)_3(s) + H_2O(g)$

balance hydrogen: $Fe_2O_3(s) + \mathbf{3}H_2SO_4(l) \rightarrow Fe_2(SO_4)_3(s) + \mathbf{3}H_2O(g)$

balanced equation: $Fe_2O_3(s) + \mathbf{3}H_2SO_4(l) \rightarrow Fe_2(SO_4)_3(s) + 3H_2O(g)$

40.   a. $Na_2SO_4(aq) + CaCl_2(aq) \rightarrow CaSO_4(s) + 2NaCl(aq)$

b. $3Fe(s) + 4H_2O(g) \rightarrow Fe_3O_4(s) + 4H_2(g)$

c. $Ca(OH)_2(aq) + 2HCl(aq) \rightarrow CaCl_2(aq) + 2H_2O(l)$

d. $Br_2(g) + 2H_2O(l) + SO_2(g) \rightarrow 2HBr(aq) + H_2SO_4(aq)$

e. $3NaOH(s) + H_3PO_4(aq) \rightarrow Na_3PO_4(aq) + 3H_2O(l)$

f. $2NaNO_3(s) \rightarrow 2NaNO_2(s) + O_2(g)$

g. $2Na_2O_2(s) + 2H_2O(l) \rightarrow 4NaOH(aq) + O_2(g)$

h. $4Si(s) + S_8(s) \rightarrow 2Si_2S_4(s)$

42. a. $4NaCl(s) + 2SO_2(g) + 2H_2O(g) + O_2(g) \rightarrow 2Na_2SO_4(s) + 4HCl(g)$

b. $3Br_2(l) + I_2(s) \rightarrow 2IBr_3(s)$

c. $Ca(s) + 2H_2O(g) \rightarrow Ca(OH)_2(aq) + H_2(g)$

d. $2BF_3(g) + 3H_2O(g) \rightarrow B_2O_3(s) + 6HF(g)$

e. $SO_2(g) + 2Cl_2(g) \rightarrow SOCl_2(l) + Cl_2O(g)$

f. $Li_2O(s) + H_2O(l) \rightarrow 2LiOH(aq)$

g. $Mg(s) + CuO(s) \rightarrow MgO(s) + Cu(l)$

h. $Fe_3O_4(s) + 4H_2(g) \rightarrow 3Fe(l) + 4H_2O(g)$

44. a. $Ba(NO_3)_2(aq) + Na_2CrO_4(aq) \rightarrow BaCrO_4(s) + 2NaNO_3(aq)$

b. $PbCl_2(aq) + K_2SO_4(aq) \rightarrow PbSO_4(s) + 2KCl(aq)$

c. $C_2H_5OH(l) + 3O_2(g) \rightarrow 2CO_2(g) + 3H_2O(l)$

d. $CaC_2(s) + 2H_2O(l) \rightarrow Ca(OH)_2(s) + C_2H_2(g)$

e. $Sr(s) + 2HNO_3(aq) \rightarrow Sr(NO_3)_2(aq) + H_2(g)$

f. $BaO_2(s) + H_2SO_4(aq) \rightarrow BaSO_4(s) + H_2O_2(aq)$

g. $2AsI_3(s) \rightarrow 2As(s) + 3I_2(s)$

h. $2CuSO_4(aq) + 4KI(s) \rightarrow 2CuI(s) + I_2(s) + 2K_2SO_4(aq)$

46. $Na(s) + O_2(g) \rightarrow Na_2O_2(s)$

$Na_2O_2(s) + H_2O(l) \rightarrow NaOH(aq) + O_2(g)$

48. $C_{12}H_{22}O_{11}(aq) + H_2O(l) \rightarrow 4C_2H_5OH(aq) + 4CO_2(g)$

50. $2Al_2O_3(s) + 3C(s) \rightarrow 4Al(s) + 3CO_2(g)$

52. $2Li(s) + S(s) \rightarrow Li_2S(s)$

$2Na(s) + S(s) \rightarrow Na_2S(s)$

$2K(s) + S(s) \rightarrow K_2S(s)$

$2Rb(s) + S(s) \rightarrow Rb_2S(s)$

$2Cs(s) + S(s) \rightarrow Cs_2S(s)$

$2Fr(s) + S(s) \rightarrow Fr_2S(s)$

54. $BaO_2(s) + H_2O(l) \rightarrow BaO(s) + H_2O_2(aq)$

56. $2KClO_3(s) \rightarrow 2KCl(s) + 3O_2(g)$

58. $NH_3(g) + HCl(g) \rightarrow NH_4Cl(s)$

60.   The senses we call "odor" and "taste" are really chemical reactions of the receptors in our body with molecules in the food we are eating. The fact that the receptors no longer detect the "fishy" odor or taste suggest that adding the lemon juice or vinegar has changed the nature of the amines in the fish.

62. $Fe(s) + S(s) \rightarrow FeS(s)$

64. $K_2CrO_4(aq) + BaCl_2(aq) \rightarrow BaCrO_4(s) + 2KCl(aq)$

66. $2NaCl(aq) + 2H_2O(l) \rightarrow 2NaOH(aq) + H_2(g) + Cl_2(g)$

    $2NaBr(aq) + 2H_2O(l) \rightarrow 2NaOH(aq) + H_2(g) + Br_2(g)$

    $2NaI(aq) + 2H_2O(l) \rightarrow 2NaOH(aq) + H_2(g) + I_2(g)$

68. $CaC_2(s) + 2H_2O(l) \rightarrow Ca(OH)_2(s) + C_2H_2(g)$

70. $CuO(s) + H_2SO_4(aq) \rightarrow CuSO_4(aq) + H_2O(l)$

72. $Na_2SO_3(aq) + S(s) \rightarrow Na_2S_2O_3(aq)$

74.   a. $Cl_2(g) + 2KI(aq) \rightarrow 2KCl(aq) + I_2(s)$

    b. $CaC_2(s) + 2H_2O(l) \rightarrow Ca(OH)_2(s) + C_2H_2(g)$

    c. $2NaCl(s) + H_2SO_4(l) \rightarrow Na_2SO_4(s) + 2HCl(g)$

    d. $CaF_2(s) + H_2SO_4(l) \rightarrow CaSO_4(s) + 2HF(g)$

    e. $K_2CO_3(s) \rightarrow K_2O(s) + CO_2(g)$

    f. $3BaO(s) + 2Al(s) \rightarrow Al_2O_3(s) + 3Ba(s)$

    g. $2Al(s) + 3F_2(g) \rightarrow 2AlF_3(s)$

    h. $CS_2(g) + 3Cl_2(g) \rightarrow CCl_4(l) + S_2Cl_2(g)$

76.   a. $Pb(NO_3)_2(aq) + K_2CrO_4(aq) \rightarrow PbCrO_4(s) + 2KNO_3(aq)$

    b. $BaCl_2(aq) + Na_2SO_4(aq) \rightarrow BaSO_4(s) + 2NaCl(aq)$

    c. $2CH_3OH(l) + 3O_2(g) \rightarrow 2CO_2(g) + 4H_2O(g)$

    d. $Na_2CO_3(aq) + S(s) + SO_2(g) \rightarrow CO_2(g) + Na_2S_2O_3(aq)$

    e. $Cu(s) + 2H_2SO_4(aq) \rightarrow CuSO_4(aq) + SO_2(g) + 2H_2O(l)$

    f. $MnO_2(s) + 4HCl(aq) \rightarrow MnCl_2(aq) + Cl_2(g) + 2H_2O(l)$

    g. $As_2O_3(s) + 6KI(aq) + 6HCl(aq) \rightarrow 2AsI_3(s) + 6KCl(aq) + 3H_2O(l)$

    h. $2Na_2S_2O_3(aq) + I_2(aq) \rightarrow Na_2S_4O_6(aq) + 2NaI(aq)$

CHAPTER 7

Reactions in Aqueous Solution

2.   Driving forces are types of *changes* in a system that push a reaction in the *direction of product formation*; driving forces discussed in Chapter 7 include: formation of a *solid*, formation of *water*, formation of a *gas*, and transfer of electrons.

4.   A reactant in aqueous solution is indicated with (*aq*). Formation of a solid is indicated with (*s*)

6.   Because each formula unit of $MgCl_2$ contains two chloride ions for each magnesium ion, that ratio will be preserved in the solution when $MgCl_2$ is dissolved in water.

8.   Chemists know that a solution contains independent ions because such a solution will readily allow an electrical current to pass through it. The simplest experiment that demonstrates this uses the sort of light–bulb conductivity apparatus described in the text: if the light bulb glows strongly, then the solution must contain a lot of ions to be conducting the electricity well.

10.   Answer depends on student choices.

12.   a.   soluble (Rule 3: most chloride salts are soluble.)

        b.   soluble (Rule 2: most salts of NH_4^+ are soluble.)

        c.   soluble (Rule 2: most salts of Na^+ are soluble.)

        d.   insoluble (Rule 5: most hydroxide compounds are insoluble.)

        e.   soluble (Rule 2: most salts of K^+ are soluble.)

        f.   soluble (Rule 1: most nitrate salts are soluble.)

        g.   soluble (Rule 4: most sulfate salts are soluble.)

        h.   insoluble (Rule 6: most sulfide salts are insoluble.)

14.   a.   Rule 6: Most sulfide salts are insoluble.

        b.   Rule 6: Most carbonate salts are insoluble.

        c.   Rule 6: Most phosphate salts are insoluble.

        d.   Rule 3: Exception to the rule for chloride salts.

        e.   Rule 4: Exception to the rule for sulfate salts.

16.   a. $MnCO_3$: Rule 6 (most carbonates are only slightly soluble).

        b. $CaSO_4$: Rule 4 (exception for sulfates).

        c. Hg_2Cl_2: Rule 3: (exception for chlorides).

        d.   soluble

e. $Ni(OH)_2$: Rule 5 (most hydroxides are only slightly soluble).

f. $BaSO_4$: Rule 4 (exception for sulfates).

18.   The formulas of the precipitates are in boldface type.

a.   Rule 6: Most carbonate salts are insoluble.

$Na_2CO_3(aq) + CuSO_4(aq) \rightarrow Na_2SO_4(aq) + \mathbf{CuCO_3(s)}$

b.   Rule 3: Exception for chloride salts.

$HCl(aq) + AgC_2H_3O_2(aq) \rightarrow HC_2H_3O_2(aq) + \mathbf{AgCl(s)}$

c.   No precipitate

d.   Rule 6: Most sulfide salts are insoluble.

$3(NH_4)_2S(aq) + 2FeCl_3(aq) \rightarrow 6NH_4Cl(aq) + \mathbf{Fe_2S_3(s)}$

e.   Rule 4: Exception for sulfate salts

$H_2SO_4(aq) + Pb(NO_3)_2(aq) \rightarrow 2HNO_3(aq) + \mathbf{PbSO_4(s)}$

f.   Rule 6: Most phosphate salts are insoluble.

$2K_3PO_4(aq) + 3CaCl_2(aq) \rightarrow 6KCl(aq) + \mathbf{Ca_3(PO_4)_2(s)}$

20.   Hint: when balancing equations involving polyatomic ions, especially in precipitation reactions, balance the polyatomic ions as a *unit*, not in terms of the atoms the polyatomic ions contain (e.g., treat nitrate ion, NO_3^- as a single entity, not as one nitrogen and three oxygen atoms). When finished balancing, however, be sure to count the individual number of atoms of each type on each side of the equation.

a. $CaCl_2 (aq) + AgNO_3 (aq) \rightarrow Ca(NO_3)_2 (aq) + AgCl (s)$

balance chlorine: $CaCl_2 (aq) + AgNO_3 (aq) \rightarrow Ca(NO_3)_2 (aq) + \mathbf{2}AgCl (s)$

balance silver: $CaCl_2 (aq) + \mathbf{2}AgNO_3 (aq) \rightarrow Ca(NO_3)_2 (aq) + 2AgCl (s)$

balanced equation: $CaCl_2 (aq) + 2AgNO_3 (aq) \rightarrow Ca(NO_3)_2 (aq) + 2AgCl (s)$

b. $AgNO_3(aq) + K_2CrO_4(aq) \rightarrow Ag_2CrO_4(s) + KNO_3(aq)$

balance silver: $\mathbf{2}AgNO_3(aq) + K_2CrO_4(aq) \rightarrow Ag_2CrO_4(s) + KNO_3(aq)$

balance nitrate ion: $2AgNO_3(aq) + K_2CrO_4(aq) \rightarrow Ag_2CrO_4(s) + \mathbf{2}KNO_3(aq)$

balanced equation: $2AgNO_3(aq) + K_2CrO_4(aq) \rightarrow Ag_2CrO_4(s) + 2KNO_3(aq)$

c. $BaCl_2(aq) + K_2SO_4(aq) \rightarrow BaSO_4(s) + KCl(aq)$

balance potassium: $BaCl_2(aq) + K_2SO_4(aq) \rightarrow BaSO_4(s) + \mathbf{2}KCl(aq)$

balanced equation: $BaCl_2(aq) + K_2SO_4(aq) \rightarrow BaSO_4(s) + 2KCl(aq)$

22.   The products are determined by having the ions "switch partners." For example, for a general reaction $AB + CD \rightarrow$, the possible products are AD and CB if the ions switch partners. If either AD or CB is insoluble, then a precipitation reaction has occurred. In the following reactions, the formula of the precipitate is given in boldface type.

a. $Na_2CO_3(aq) + K_2SO_4(aq) \rightarrow$ no precipitate; all combinations are soluble

b. $CuCl_2(aq) + (NH_4)_2CO_3(aq) \rightarrow 2NH_4Cl(aq) + \mathbf{CuCO_3(s)}$

Rule 6: Most carbonate salts are only slightly soluble.

c. $K_3PO_4(aq) + AlCl_3(aq) \rightarrow 3KCl(aq) + \mathbf{AlPO_4(s)}$

Rule 6: Most phosphate salts are only slightly soluble.

24. Spectator ions are ions which *remain in solution* during a precipitation/double displacement reaction. For example in the reaction

$$BaCl_2(aq) + K_2SO_4(aq) \rightarrow BaSO_4(s) + 2KCl(aq)$$

the K^+ and Cl^- ions are the spectator ions.

26. The net ionic equation for a reaction indicates *only those ions that go to form the precipitate* and does not show the spectator ions present in the solutes mixed. The identity of the precipitate is determined from the Solubility Rules (Table 7.1).

a. $Ca(NO_3)_2(aq) + H_2SO_4(aq) \rightarrow CaSO_4(s) + 2HNO_3(aq)$

$Ca^{2+}(aq) + SO_4^{2-}(aq) \rightarrow CaSO_4(s)$

b. $Ni(NO_3)_2(aq) + 2NaOH(aq) \rightarrow Ni(OH)_2(s) + 2NaNO_3(aq)$

$Ni^{2+}(aq) + 2OH^-(aq) \rightarrow Ni(OH)_2(s)$

c. $3(NH_4)_2S(aq) + 2FeCl_3(aq) \rightarrow Fe_2S_3(s) + 6NH_4Cl(aq)$

$2Fe^{3+}(aq) + 3S^{2-}(aq) \rightarrow Fe_2S_3(s)$

28. $Ag^+(aq) + Cl^-(aq) \rightarrow AgCl(s)$

$Pb^{2+}(aq) + 2Cl^-(aq) \rightarrow PbCl_2(s)$

$Hg_2^{2+}(aq) + 2Cl^-(aq) \rightarrow Hg_2Cl_2(s)$

30. $Co^{2+}(aq) + S^{2-}(aq) \rightarrow CoS(s)$

$2Co^{3+}(aq) + 3S^{2-}(aq) \rightarrow Co_2S_3(s)$

$Fe^{2+}(aq) + S^{2-}(aq) \rightarrow FeS(s)$

$2Fe^{3+}(aq) + 3S^{2-}(aq) \rightarrow Fe_2S_3(s)$

32. Strong bases fully produce hydroxide ions when dissolved in water. The strong bases are also strong electrolytes.

34. acids: HCl, H_2SO_4, HNO_3, $HClO_4$, HBr

bases: $NaOH$, KOH, $RbOH$, $CsOH$

36. A salt is the ionic product remaining in solution when an acid neutralizes a base. For example, in the reaction $HCl (aq) + NaOH(aq) \rightarrow NaCl(aq) + H_2O(l)$ sodium chloride is the salt produced by the neutralization reaction.

38. $RbOH(s) \rightarrow Rb^+(aq) + OH^-(aq)$

$CsOH(s) \rightarrow Cs^+(aq) + OH^-(aq)$

40.   In general, the salt formed in an aqueous acid–base reaction consists of the *positive ion of the base* involved in the reaction, combined with the *negative ion of the acid*. The hydrogen ion of the strong acid combines with the hydroxide ion of the strong base to produce water, which is the other product of the acid–base reactions.

a. $H_2SO_4(aq) + 2KOH(aq) \rightarrow K_2SO_4(aq) + 2H_2O(l)$

b. $HNO_3(aq) + NaOH(aq) \rightarrow NaNO_3(aq) + H_2O(l)$

c. $2HCl(aq) + Ca(OH)_2(aq) \rightarrow CaCl_2(aq) + 2H_2O(l)$

d. $2HClO_4(aq) + Ba(OH)_2(aq) \rightarrow Ba(ClO_4)_2(aq) + 2H_2O(l)$

42.   Answer depends on student choice of example: $Na(s) + Cl_2(g) \rightarrow 2NaCl(s)$ is an example.

44.   The metallic element *loses* electrons and the nonmetallic element *gains* electrons.

46.   Each magnesium atom would lose two electrons. Each oxygen atom would gain two electrons (so the O_2 molecule would gain four electrons). Two magnesium atoms would be required to react with each oxygen, O_2, molecule. Magnesium ions are charged 2+, oxide ions are charged 2–.

48.   Each potassium atom loses one electron. The sulfur atom gains two electrons. So two potassium atoms are required to react with one sulfur atom.

$2 \times (K \rightarrow K^+ + e^-)$

$S + 2e^- \rightarrow S^{2-}$

50.   a. $P_4(s) + O_2(g) \rightarrow P_4O_{10}(s)$

balance oxygen: $P_4(s) + \mathbf{5}O_2(g) \rightarrow P_4O_{10}(s)$

balanced equation: $P_4(s) + 5O_2(g) \rightarrow P_4O_{10}(s)$

b. $MgO(s) + C(s) \rightarrow Mg(s) + CO(g)$

This equation is already balanced.

c. $Sr(s) + H_2O(l) \rightarrow Sr(OH)_2(aq) + H_2(g)$

balance oxygen: $Sr(s) + \mathbf{2}H_2O(l) \rightarrow Sr(OH)_2(aq) + H_2(g)$

balanced equation: $Sr(s) + 2H_2O(l) \rightarrow Sr(OH)_2(aq) + H_2(g)$

d. $Co(s) + HCl(aq) \rightarrow CoCl_2(aq) + H_2(g)$

balance hydrogen: $Co(s) + \mathbf{2}HCl(aq) \rightarrow CoCl_2(aq) + H_2(g)$

balanced equation: $Co(s) + 2HCl(aq) \rightarrow CoCl_2(aq) + H_2(g)$

52.   A reaction must be an oxidation–reduction reaction if any of the oxidation numbers of the atoms in the equation change. Aluminum changes oxidation state from 0 in Al to +3 (oxidation) in Al_2O_3 and $AlCl_3$; nitrogen changes oxidation state from –3 in NH_4^+ to +2 in NO (oxidation); chlorine changes oxidation state from +7 in ClO_4^- to –1 in $AlCl_3$ (reduction)

54. For each reaction, the type of reaction is first identified, followed by some of the reasoning that leads to this choice (there may be more than one way in which you can recognize a particular type of reaction).

   a. oxidation–reduction (Oxygen changes from the combined state to the elemental state.)

   b. oxidation–reduction (Zinc changes from the elemental to the combined state; hydrogen changes from the combined to the elemental state.)

   c. acid–base (H_2SO_4 is a strong acid and NaOH is a strong base; water and a salt are formed.)

   d. acid–base, precipitation (H_2SO_4 is a strong acid, and $Ba(OH)_2$ is a base; water and a salt are formed; an insoluble product forms.)

   e. precipitation (From the Solubility Rules of Table 7.1, AgCl is only slightly soluble.)

   f. precipitation (From the Solubility Rules of Table 7.1, $Cu(OH)_2$ is only slightly soluble.)

   g. oxidation–reduction (Chlorine and fluorine change from the elemental to the combined state.)

   h. oxidation–reduction (Oxygen changes from the elemental to the combined state.)

   i. acid–base (HNO_3 is a strong acid and $Ca(OH)_2$ is a strong base; a salt and water are formed.)

56. oxidation–reduction

58. A decomposition reaction is one in which a given compound is broken down into simpler compounds or constituent elements. The reactions

$$CaCO_3(s) \rightarrow CaO(s) + CO_2(g)$$

$$2HgO(s) \rightarrow 2Hg(l) + O_2(g)$$

both represent decomposition reactions. Such reactions often (but not necessarily always) may be classified in other ways. For example, the reaction of $HgO(s)$ is also an oxidation–reduction reaction.

60. Compounds like those in this problem, containing only carbon and hydrogen, are called *hydrocarbons*. When a hydrocarbon is reacted with oxygen (O_2), the hydrocarbon is almost always converted to carbon dioxide and water vapor. Because water molecules contain an odd number of oxygen atoms, and O_2 contains an even number of oxygen atoms, it is often difficult to balance such equations. For this reason, it is simpler to balance the equation using fractional coefficients if necessary, and then to multiply by a factor that will give whole number coefficients for the final balanced equation.

   a. $C_3H_8(g) + O_2(g) \rightarrow CO_2(g) + H_2O(g)$

   balance carbon: $C_3H_8(g) + O_2(g) \rightarrow \mathbf{3}CO_2(g) + H_2O(g)$

   balance hydrogen: $C_3H_8(g) + O_2(g) \rightarrow 3CO_2(g) + \mathbf{4}H_2O(g)$

   balance oxygen: $C_3H_8(g) + \mathbf{5}O_2(g) \rightarrow 3CO_2(g) + 4H_2O(g)$

   balanced equation: $C_3H_8(g) + 5O_2(g) \rightarrow 3CO_2(g) + 4H_2O(g)$

b. $C_2H_4(g) + O_2(g) \rightarrow CO_2(g) + H_2O(g)$

balance carbon: $C_2H_4(g) + O_2(g) \rightarrow \mathbf{2}CO_2(g) + H_2O(g)$

balance hydrogen: $C_2H_4(g) + O_2(g) \rightarrow \mathbf{2}CO_2(g) + \mathbf{2}H_2O(g)$

balance oxygen: $C_2H_4(g) + \mathbf{3}O_2(g) \rightarrow 2CO_2(g) + 2H_2O(g)$

balanced equation: $C_2H_4(g) + 3O_2(g) \rightarrow 2CO_2(g) + 2H_2O(g)$

c. $C_4H_{10}(g) + O_2(g) \rightarrow CO_2(g) + H_2O(g)$

balance carbon: $C_4H_{10}(g) + O_2(g) \rightarrow \mathbf{4}CO_2(g) + H_2O(g)$

balance hydrogen: $C_4H_{10}(g) + O_2(g) \rightarrow 4CO_2(g) + \mathbf{5}H_2O(g)$

balance oxygen: $C_4H_{10}(g) + \frac{13}{2}O_2(g) \rightarrow 4CO_2(g) + 5H_2O(g)$

balanced equation: $2C_4H_{10}(g) + 13O_2(g) \rightarrow 8CO_2(g) + 10H_2O(g)$

62.   A reaction in which small molecules or atoms combine to make a larger molecule is called a *synthesis* reaction. An example would be the synthesis of sodium chloride from the elements

$$2Na(s) + Cl_2(g) \rightarrow 2NaCl(s).$$

A reaction in which a molecule is broken down into simpler molecules or atoms is called a *decomposition* reaction. An example would be the decomposition of sodium hydrogen carbonate when heated.

$$2NaHCO_3(s) \rightarrow Na_2CO_3(s) + CO_2(g) + H_2O(g).$$

Specific examples will depend on the students' input.

64.   a. $8Fe(s) + S_8(s) \rightarrow 8FeS(s)$

b. $4Co(s) + 3O_2(g) \rightarrow 2Co_2O_3(s)$

c. $Cl_2O_7(g) + H_2O(l) \rightarrow 2HClO_4(aq)$

66.   a. $2Al(s) + 3Br_2(l) \rightarrow 2AlBr_3(s)$

b. $Zn(s) + 2HClO_4(aq) \rightarrow Zn(ClO_4)_2(aq) + H_2(g)$

c. $3Na(s) + P(s) \rightarrow Na_3P(s)$

d. $CH_4(g) + 4Cl_2(g) \rightarrow CCl_4(l) + 4HCl(g)$

e. $Cu(s) + 2AgNO_3(aq) \rightarrow Cu(NO_3)_2(aq) + 2Ag(s)$

68.   In several cases, the given ion may be precipitated by *many* reactants. The following are only three of the possible examples.

a.   Chloride ion would precipitate when treated with solutions containing silver ion, lead(II) ion, or mercury(I) ion.

$Ag^+(aq) + Cl^-(aq) \rightarrow AgCl(s)$

$Pb^{2+}(aq) + 2Cl^-(aq) \rightarrow PbCl_2(s)$

$Hg_2^{2+}(aq) + 2Cl^-(aq) \rightarrow Hg_2Cl_2(s)$

b.   Calcium ion would precipitate when treated with solutions containing sulfate ion, carbonate ion, and phosphate ion.

$$Ca^{2+}(aq) + SO_4^{2-}(aq) \rightarrow CaSO_4(s)$$

$$Ca^{2+}(aq) + CO_3^{2-}(aq) \rightarrow CaCO_3(s)$$

$$3Ca^{2+}(aq) + 2PO_4^{3-}(aq) \rightarrow Ca_3(PO_4)_2(s)$$

c.   Iron(III) ion would precipitate when treated with solutions containing hydroxide, sulfide, or carbonate ions.

$$Fe^{3+}(aq) + 3OH^-(aq) \rightarrow Fe(OH)_3(s)$$

$$2Fe^{3+}(aq) + 3S^{2-}(aq) \rightarrow Fe_2S_3(s)$$

$$2Fe^{3+}(aq) + 3CO_3^{2-}(aq) \rightarrow Fe_2(CO_3)_3(s)$$

d.   Sulfate ion would precipitate when treated with solutions containing barium ion, calcium ion, or lead(II) ion.

$$Ba^{2+}(aq) + SO_4^{2-}(aq) \rightarrow BaSO_4(s)$$

$$Ca^{2+}(aq) + SO_4^{2-}(aq) \rightarrow CaSO_4(s)$$

$$Pb^{2+}(aq) + SO_4^{2-}(aq) \rightarrow PbSO_4(s)$$

e.   Mercury(I) ion would precipitate when treated with solutions containing chloride ion, sulfide ion, or carbonate ion.

$$Hg_2^{2+}(aq) + 2Cl^-(aq) \rightarrow Hg_2Cl_2(s)$$

$$Hg_2^{2+}(aq) + S^{2-}(aq) \rightarrow Hg_2S(s)$$

$$Hg_2^{2+}(aq) + CO_3^{2-}(aq) \rightarrow Hg_2CO_3(s)$$

f.   Silver ion would precipitate when treated with solutions containing chloride ion, sulfide ion, or carbonate ion.

$$Ag^+(aq) + Cl^-(aq) \rightarrow AgCl(s)$$

$$2Ag^+(aq) + S^{2-}(aq) \rightarrow Ag_2S(s)$$

$$2Ag^+(aq) + CO_3^{2-}(aq) \rightarrow Ag_2CO_3(s)$$

70.   The formulas of the salts are indicated in boldface type.

a. $HNO_3(aq) + KOH(aq) \rightarrow H_2O(l) + \mathbf{KNO_3}(aq)$

b. $H_2SO_4(aq) + Ba(OH)_2(aq) \rightarrow 2H_2O(l) + \mathbf{BaSO_4}(s)$

c. $HClO_4(aq) + NaOH(aq) \rightarrow H_2O(l) + \mathbf{NaClO_4}(aq)$

d. $2HCl(aq) + Ca(OH)_2(aq) \rightarrow 2H_2O(l) + \mathbf{CaCl_2}(aq)$

72.   a.   soluble (Rule 2: Most potassium salts are soluble.)

b.   soluble (Rule 2: Most ammonium salts are soluble.)

c.   insoluble (Rule 6: Most carbonate salts are only slightly soluble.)

d.   insoluble (Rule 6: Most phosphate salts are only slightly soluble.)

e.   soluble (Rule 2: Most sodium salts are soluble.)

f. insoluble (Rule 6: Most carbonate salts are only slightly soluble.)

g. soluble (Rule 3: Most chloride salts are soluble.)

74. The precipitates are marked in boldface type.

a. Rule 3: AgCl is listed as an exception

$$AgNO_3(aq) + HCl(aq) \rightarrow \textbf{AgCl}(s) + HNO_3(aq)$$

b. Rule 6: Most carbonate salts are only slightly soluble.

$$CuSO_4(aq) + (NH_4)_2CO_3(aq) \rightarrow \textbf{CuCO}_3(s) + (NH_4)_2SO_4(aq)$$

c. Rule 6: Most carbonate salts are only slightly soluble.

$$FeSO_4(aq) + K_2CO_3(aq) \rightarrow \textbf{FeCO}_3(s) + K_2SO_4(aq)$$

d. no reaction

e. Rule 6: Most carbonate salts are only slightly soluble.

$$Pb(NO_3)_2(aq) + Li_2CO_3(aq) \rightarrow \textbf{PbCO}_3(s) + 2LiNO_3(aq)$$

f. Rule 5: Most hydroxide compounds are only slightly soluble.

$$SnCl_4(aq) + 4NaOH(aq) \rightarrow \textbf{Sn(OH)}_4(s) + 4NaCl(aq)$$

76. $Fe^{2+}(aq) + S^{2-}(aq) \rightarrow FeS(s)$

$2Cr^{3+}(aq) + 3S^{2-}(aq) \rightarrow Cr_2S_3(s)$

$Ni^{2+}(aq) + S^{2-}(aq) \rightarrow NiS(s)$

78. These anions tend to form insoluble precipitates with *many* metal ions. The following are illustrative for cobalt(II) chloride, tin(II) chloride, and copper(II) nitrate reacting with the sodium salts of the given anions.

a. $CoCl_2(aq) + Na_2S(aq) \rightarrow CoS(s) + 2NaCl(aq)$

$SnCl_2(aq) + Na_2S(aq) \rightarrow SnS(s) + 2NaCl(aq)$

$Cu(NO_3)_2(aq) + Na_2S(aq) \rightarrow CuS(s) + 2NaNO_3(aq)$

b. $CoCl_2(aq) + Na_2CO_3(aq) \rightarrow CoCO_3(s) + 2NaCl(aq)$

$SnCl_2(aq) + Na_2CO_3(aq) \rightarrow SnCO_3(s) + 2NaCl(aq)$

$Cu(NO_3)_2(aq) + Na_2CO_3(aq) \rightarrow CuCO_3(s) + 2NaNO_3(aq)$

c. $CoCl_2(aq) + 2NaOH(aq) \rightarrow Co(OH)_2(s) + 2NaCl(aq)$

$SnCl_2(aq) + 2NaOH(aq) \rightarrow Sn(OH)_2(s) + 2NaCl(aq)$

$Cu(NO_3)_2(aq) + 2NaOH(aq) \rightarrow Cu(OH)_2(s) + 2NaNO_3(aq)$

d. $3CoCl_2(aq) + 2Na_3PO_4(aq) \rightarrow Co_3(PO_4)_2(s) + 6NaCl(aq)$

$3SnCl_2(aq) + 2Na_3PO_4(aq) \rightarrow Sn_3(PO_4)_2(s) + 6NaCl(aq)$

$3Cu(NO_3)_2(aq) + 2Na_3PO_4(aq) \rightarrow Cu_3(PO_4)_2(s) + 6NaNO_3(aq)$

80. a. $Na + O_2 \rightarrow Na_2O_2$

    Balance sodium: $\mathbf{2}Na + O_2 \rightarrow Na_2O_2$

    Balanced equation: $2Na(s) + O_2(g) \rightarrow Na_2O_2(s)$

    b. $Fe(s) + H_2SO_4(aq) \rightarrow FeSO_4(aq) + H_2(g)$

    Equation is already balanced!

    c. $Al_2O_3 \rightarrow Al + O_2$

    Balance oxygen: $\mathbf{2}Al_2O_3 \rightarrow Al + \mathbf{3}O_2$

    Balance aluminum: $2Al_2O_3 \rightarrow \mathbf{4}Al + 3O_2$

    Balanced equation: $2Al_2O_3(s) \rightarrow 4Al(s) + 3O_2(g)$

    d. $Fe + Br_2 \rightarrow FeBr_3$

    Balance bromine: $Fe + \mathbf{3}Br_2 \rightarrow \mathbf{2}FeBr_3$

    Balance iron: $\mathbf{2}Fe + 3Br_2 \rightarrow 2FeBr_3$

    Balanced equation: $2Fe(s) + 3Br_2(l) \rightarrow 2FeBr_3(s)$

    e. $Zn + HNO_3 \rightarrow Zn(NO_3)_2 + H_2$

    Balance nitrate ions: $Zn + \mathbf{2}HNO_3 \rightarrow Zn(NO_3)_2 + H_2$

    Balanced equation: $Zn(s) + 2HNO_3(aq) \rightarrow Zn(NO_3)_2(aq) + H_2(g)$

82. a. $2C_4H_{10}(l) + 13O_2(g) \rightarrow 8CO_2(g) + 10H_2O(g)$

    b. $C_4H_{10}O(l) + 6O_2(g) \rightarrow 4CO_2(g) + 5H_2O(g)$

    c. $2C_4H_{10}O_2(l) + 11O_2(g) \rightarrow 8CO_2(g) + 10H_2O(g)$

84. a. $2NaHCO_3(s) \rightarrow Na_2CO_3(s) + H_2O(g) + CO_2(g)$

    b. $2NaClO_3(s) \rightarrow 2NaCl(s) + 3O_2(g)$

    c. $2HgO(s) \rightarrow 2Hg(l) + O_2(g)$

    d. $C_{12}H_{22}O_{11}(s) \rightarrow 12C(s) + 11H_2O(g)$

    e. $2H_2O_2(l) \rightarrow 2H_2O(l) + O_2(g)$

86. $Al(s) + H_2SO_4(aq) \rightarrow Al_2(SO_4)_3(aq) + H_2(g)$

    $Zn(s) + H_2SO_4(aq) \rightarrow ZnSO_4(aq) + H_2(g)$

    $Mg(s) + H_2SO_4(aq) \rightarrow MgSO_4(aq) + H_2(g)$

    $Co(s) + H_2SO_4(aq) \rightarrow CoSO_4(aq) + H_2(g)$

    $Ni(s) + H_2SO_4(aq) \rightarrow NiSO_4(aq) + H_2(g)$

88. a. one

    b. one

    c. two

d.   two

e.   three

90.   A very simple example that fits the bill is: $C(s) + O_2(g) \rightarrow CO_2(g)$

92.   a. $2C_3H_8O(l) + 9O_2(g) \rightarrow 6CO_2(g) + 8H_2O(g)$

oxidation–reduction, combustion

b. $HCl(aq) + AgC_2H_3O_2(aq) \rightarrow AgCl(s) + HC_2H_3O_2(aq)$

precipitation, double–displacement

c. $3HCl(aq) + Al(OH)_3(s) \rightarrow AlCl_3(aq) + 3H_2O(l)$

acid–base, double–displacement

d. $2H_2O_2(aq) \rightarrow 2H_2O(l) + O_2(g)$

oxidation–reduction, decomposition

e. $N_2H_4(l) + O_2(g) \rightarrow N_2(g) + 2H_2O(g)$

oxidation–reduction, combustion

94. $2Na(s) + Cl_2(g) \rightarrow 2NaCl(s)$

$2Al(s) + 3Cl_2(g) \rightarrow 2AlCl_3(s)$

$Zn(s) + Cl_2(g) \rightarrow ZnCl_2(s)$

$Ca(s) + Cl_2(g) \rightarrow CaCl_2(s)$

$2Fe(s) + 3Cl_2(g) \rightarrow 2FeCl_3(s)$; $Fe(s) + Cl_2(g) \rightarrow FeCl_2(s)$

CUMULATIVE REVIEW

Chapters 6 and 7

2.   A chemical equation indicates the substances necessary for a chemical reaction to take place, as well as what is produced by that chemical reaction. The substances to the left of the arrow in a chemical equation are called the reactants; those to the right of the arrow are referred to as the products. In addition, if a chemical equation has been balanced, then the equation indicates the relative proportions in which the reactant molecules combine to form the product molecules.

4.   It is *never* permissible to change the subscripts of a formula when balancing a chemical equation: changing the subscripts changes the *identity* of a substance from one chemical to another. For example, consider the unbalanced chemical equation

$$H_2(g) + O_2(g) \rightarrow H_2O(l).$$

If you changed the *formula* of the product from $H_2O(l)$ to $H_2O_2(l)$, the equation would appear to be "balanced". However, H_2O is water, whereas H_2O_2 is hydrogen peroxide–a completely different chemical substance (which is not prepared by reaction of the elements hydrogen and oxygen).

When we balance a chemical equation, it is permitted only to adjust the *coefficients* of a formula, so changing a coefficient merely changes the number of molecules of a substance being used in the reaction, without changing the identity of the substance. For the example above, we can balance the equation by putting coefficients of 2 in front of the formulas of H_2 and H_2O: these coefficients do not change the nature of what is reacting and what product is formed.

$$2H_2(g) + O_2(g) \rightarrow 2H_2O(l)$$

6.   A precipitation reaction is one in which a *solid* forms when the reactants are combined: the solid is called a precipitate. The driving force in such a reaction is the formation of the solid, thus *removing ions* from the solution. There are many examples of such precipitation reactions: consult the solubility rules in Table 7.1 if you need help. One example would be to combine barium nitrate and sodium carbonate solutions: a precipitate of barium carbonate would form.

The molecular equation for this reaction is:

$$Ba(NO_3)_2(aq) + Na_2CO_3(aq) \rightarrow BaCO_3(s) + 2NaNO_3(aq)$$

The net ionic equation for this reaction is:

$$Ba^{2+}(aq) + CO_3^{2-}(aq) \rightarrow BaCO_3(s)$$

8.   In summary, nearly all compounds containing the nitrate, sodium, potassium, and ammonium ions are soluble in water. Most salts containing the chloride and sulfate ions are soluble in water, with specific exceptions (see Table 7.1 for these exceptions). Most compounds containing the hydroxide, sulfide, carbonate, and phosphate ions are not soluble in water, unless the compound also contains one of the cations mentioned above (Na^+, K^+, NH_4^+).

The solubility rules are phrased as if you had a sample of a given solute and wanted to see if you could dissolve it in water. These rules can also be applied, however, to predict the identity of the solid produced in a precipitation reaction: a given combination of ions will not be soluble in water whether you take a pure compound out of a reagent bottle or if you generate the insoluble combination of ions during a chemical reaction. For example, the solubility rules say that $BaSO_4$ is not soluble in water. This means not only that a pure sample of $BaSO_4$ taken from a reagent bottle will not dissolve in water, but also that if Ba^{2+} ion and SO_4^{2-} ion end up together in the same solution, they will precipitate as $BaSO_4$. If we were to combine barium chloride and sulfuric acid solutions

$$BaCl_2(aq) + H_2SO_4(aq) \rightarrow BaSO_4(s) + 2HCl(aq)$$

then, because barium sulfate is not soluble in water, a precipitate of $BaSO_4(s)$ would form. Because a precipitate of $BaSO_4(s)$ would form no matter what barium compound or what sulfate compound were mixed, we can write the net ionic equation for the reaction as

$$Ba^{2+}(aq) + SO_4^{2-}(aq) \rightarrow BaSO_4(s).$$

Thus if, for example, barium nitrate solution were combined with sodium sulfate solution, a precipitate of $BaSO_4$ would form. Barium sulfate is insoluble in water regardless of its source.

10. Acids (such as the citric acid found in citrus fruits and the acetic acid found in vinegar) were first noted primarily because of their sour taste. The first bases noted were characterized by their bitter taste and slippery feel on the skin. Acids and bases chemically react with (neutralize) each other forming water: the net ionic equation is

$$H^+(aq) + OH^-(aq) \rightarrow H_2O(l).$$

The *strong* acids and bases fully ionize when they dissolve in water: because these substances fully ionize, they are strong electrolytes. The common strong acids are HCl(hydrochloric), HNO_3(nitric), H_2SO_4(sulfuric), and $HClO_4$(perchloric). The most common strong bases are the alkali metal hydroxides, particularly NaOH(sodium hydroxide) and KOH(potassium hydroxide).

12. Oxidation–reduction reactions are electron-transfer reactions. Oxidation represents a loss of electrons by an atom, molecule, or ion, whereas reduction is the gain of electrons by such a species. Because an oxidation–reduction process represents the transfer of electrons between species, you can't have one without the other also taking place: the electrons lost by one species must be gained by some other species. An example of a simple oxidation–reduction reaction between a metal and a nonmetal could be the following

$$Mg(s) + F_2(g) \rightarrow MgF_2(s).$$

In this process, Mg atoms lose two electrons each to become Mg^{2+} ions in MgF_2: Mg is oxidized. Each F atom of F_2 gains one electron to become a F^- ion, for a total of two electrons gained for each F_2 molecule: F_2 is reduced.

$$Mg \rightarrow Mg^{2+} + 2e^-$$

$$2(F + e^- \rightarrow F^-)$$

14. In general, a synthesis reaction represents the reaction of elements or simple compounds to produce more complex substances. There are many examples of synthesis reactions, for example

$$N_2(g) + 3H_2(g) \rightarrow 2NH_3(g)$$

$$NaOH(aq) + CO_2(g) \rightarrow NaHCO_3(s).$$

Decomposition reactions represent the breakdown of a more complex substance into simpler substances. There are many examples of decomposition reactions, for example

$$2H_2O_2(aq) \rightarrow 2H_2O(l) + O_2(g).$$

Synthesis and decomposition reactions are very often also oxidation–reduction reactions, especially if an elemental substance reacts or is generated. It is not necessary, however, for synthesis and decomposition reactions to always involve oxidation–reduction. The reaction between NaOH and CO_2 given as an example of a synthesis reaction does *not* represent oxidation–reduction.

16.   a. $C(s) + O_2(g) \rightarrow CO_2(g)$

   b. $2C(s) + O_2(g) \rightarrow 2CO(g)$

   c. $2Li(l) + 2C(s) \rightarrow Li_2C_2(s)$

   d. $FeO(s) + C(s) \rightarrow Fe(l) + CO(g)$

   e. $C(s) + 2F_2(g) \rightarrow CF_4(g)$

18.   a. $Ba(NO_3)_2(aq) + K_2CrO_4(aq) \rightarrow BaCrO_4(s) + 2KNO_3(aq)$

   b. $NaOH(aq) + CH_3COOH(aq) \rightarrow H_2O(l) + NaCH_3COO(aq)$ (then evaporate the water from the solution)

   c. $AgNO_3(aq) + NaCl(aq) \rightarrow AgCl(s) + NaNO_3(aq)$

   d. $Pb(NO_3)_2(aq) + H_2SO_4(aq) \rightarrow PbSO_4(s) + 2HNO_3(aq)$

   e. $2NaOH(aq) + H_2SO_4(aq) \rightarrow Na_2SO_4(aq) + 2H_2O(l)$ (then evaporate the water from the solution)

   f. $Ba(NO_3)_2(aq) + Na_2CO_3(aq) \rightarrow BaCO_3(s) + 2NaNO_3(aq)$

20.   a. $FeO(s) + 2HNO_3(aq) \rightarrow Fe(NO_3)_2(aq) + H_2O(l)$

      acid–base, double-displacement

   b. $2Mg(s) + 2CO_2(g) + O_2(g) \rightarrow 2MgCO_3(s)$

      synthesis; oxidation–reduction

   c. $2NaOH(s) + CuSO_4(aq) \rightarrow Cu(OH)_2(s) + Na_2SO_4(aq)$

      precipitation, double-displacement

   d. $HI(aq) + KOH(aq) \rightarrow KI(aq) + H_2O(l)$

      acid–base, double–displacement

   e. $C_3H_8(g) + 5O_2(g) \rightarrow 3CO_2(g) + 4H_2O(g)$

      combustion; oxidation–reduction

   f. $Co(NH_3)_6Cl_2(s) \rightarrow CoCl_2(s) + 6NH_3(g)$

      decomposition

   g. $2HCl(aq) + Pb(C_2H_3O_2)_2(aq) \rightarrow 2HC_2H_3O_2(aq) + PbCl_2(s)$

      precipitation, double-displacement

h. $C_{12}H_{22}O_{11}(s) \rightarrow 12C(s) + 11H_2O(g)$

decomposition; oxidation–reduction

i. $2Al(s) + 6HNO_3(aq) \rightarrow 2Al(NO_3)_3(aq) + 3H_2(g)$

oxidation–reduction; single-displacement

j. $4B(s) + 3O_2(g) \rightarrow 2B_2O_3(s)$

synthesis; oxidation–reduction

22.   Specific examples will depend on students' responses. The following are general equations that illustrate each type of reaction:

precipitation: typical when solutions of two ionic solutes are mixed, and one of the new combinations of ions is insoluble.

$A^+B^-(aq) + C^+D^-(aq) \rightarrow AD(s) + C^+D^-(aq)$

single displacement: one element replaces a less reactive element from a compound.

$A(s) + B^+C^-(aq) \rightarrow A^+C^-(aq) + B(s)$

combustion: a rapid oxidation reaction, most commonly involving $O_2(g)$. Most examples in the text involve the combustion of hydrocarbons or hydrocarbon derivatives.

(hydrocarbon or derivative) $+ O_2(g) \rightarrow CO_2(g) + H_2O(g)$

synthesis: elements or simple compounds combine to make more complicated molecules.

$A(s) + B(s) \rightarrow AB(s)$

oxidation–reduction: reactions in which electrons are transferred from one species to another. Examples of oxidation–reduction reactions include single-displacement, combustion, synthesis, and decomposition reactions.

decomposition: a compound breaks down into elements and/or simpler compounds.

$AB(s) \rightarrow A(s) + B(s)$

acid–base neutralization: a neutralization takes place when a proton from an acid combines with a hydroxide ion from a base to make a water molecule.

24.   a.   no reaction (all combinations are soluble)

b. $Ca^{2+}(aq) + SO_4^{2-}(aq) \rightarrow CaSO_4(s)$

c. $Pb^{2+}(aq) + S^{2-}(aq) \rightarrow PbS(s)$

d. $2Fe^{3+}(aq) + 3CO_3^{2-}(aq) \rightarrow Fe_2(CO_3)_3(s)$

e. $Hg_2^{2+}(aq) + 2Cl^-(aq) \rightarrow Hg_2Cl_2(s)$

f. $Ag^+(aq) + Cl^-(aq) \rightarrow AgCl(s)$

g. $3Ca^{2+}(aq) + 2PO_4^{3-}(aq) \rightarrow Ca_3(PO_4)_2(s)$

Since phosphoric acid is not a very strong acid, a more realistic equation might be

$3Ca^{2+}(aq) + 2H_3PO_4(aq) \rightarrow Ca_3(PO_4)_2(s) + 6H^+(aq)$

h.   no reaction (all combinations are soluble)

CHAPTER 8

Chemical Composition

2. The empirical formula is CFH from the structure given. The empirical formula represents the smallest whole number ratio of the number and types of atoms present.

4. The average atomic mass takes into account the various isotopes of an element and the relative abundances in which those isotopes are found.

6. a. $40.08 \text{ amu Ca} \times \dfrac{1 \text{ Ca atom}}{40.08 \text{ amu}} = 1 \text{ Ca atom}$

    b. $919.5 \text{ amu W} \times \dfrac{1 \text{ W atom}}{183.9 \text{ amu}} = 5 \text{ W atoms}$

    c. $549.4 \text{ amu Mn} \times \dfrac{1 \text{ Mn atom}}{54.94 \text{ amu}} = 10 \text{ Mn atoms}$

    d. $6345 \text{ amu I} \times \dfrac{1 \text{ I atom}}{126.9 \text{ amu}} = 50 \text{ I atoms}$

    e. $2072 \text{ amu} \times \dfrac{1 \text{ Pb atom}}{207.2 \text{ amu}} = 10 \text{ Pb atoms}$

8. One tin atom has a mass of 118.7 amu.

    A sample containing 35 tin atoms would weigh: $35 \times \dfrac{118.7 \text{ amu}}{1 \text{ atom}} = 4155 \text{ amu};$

    2967.5 amu of tin would represent: $2967.5 \text{ amu} \times \dfrac{1 \text{ tin atom}}{118.7 \text{ amu}} = 25 \text{ tin atoms.}$

10. 26.98 g (1.00 mol)

12. Since 10.09 g of neon represents half the molar mass of neon (20.18 g), then 10.09 g of neon contains

    $\frac{1}{2} \times (6.022 \times 10^{23}) = 3.011 \times 10^{23}$ neon atoms (0.500 mol).

    Also, 0.500 mol of helium gas would contain the same number of atoms as 0.500 mol of neon gas: this would be

    $\frac{1}{2} \times 4.003 \text{ g} = 2.002 \text{ g of helium gas.}$

14. The ratio of the atomic mass of Co to the atomic mass of F is (58.93 amu/19.00 amu), and the mass of cobalt is given by

$$57.0 \text{ g} \times \frac{58.93 \text{ amu}}{19.00 \text{ amu}} = 177 \text{ g Co.}$$

16. mass of a carbon atom $= 4.48 \times 10^{-23} \text{ g} \times \dfrac{12.01 \text{ amu C}}{26.98 \text{ amu Al}} = 1.99 \times 10^{-23} \text{ g}$

18. $0.50 \text{ mol Ne atoms} \times \dfrac{20.18 \text{ g}}{1 \text{ mol}} = 10.09 \text{ g Ne} = 10.\text{ g Ne (two significant figures)}$

    $1 \text{ mol B atoms} \times \dfrac{10.81 \text{ g B}}{1 \text{ mol}} = 10.81 \text{ g B} = 11 \text{ g B (two significant figures)}$

    The neon sample weighs less.

20. a. $66.50 \text{ g F} \times \dfrac{1 \text{ mol}}{19.00 \text{ g}} = 3.500 \text{ mol of F atoms}$

    b. $401.2 \text{ mg Hg} \times \dfrac{1 \text{ mmol}}{200.6 \text{ mg}} = 2.000 \text{ mmol Hg} (1 \text{ mmol} = 1/1000 \text{ mol})$

    c. $84.27 \text{ g Si} \times \dfrac{1 \text{ mol}}{28.09 \text{ g}} = 3.000 \text{ mol Si}$

    d. $48.78 \text{ g Pt} \times \dfrac{1 \text{ mol}}{195.1 \text{ g}} = 0.2500 \text{ mol Pt}$

    e. $2431 \text{ g Mg} \times \dfrac{1 \text{ mol}}{24.31 \text{ g}} = 100.0 \text{ mol Mg}$

    f. $47.97 \text{ g} \times \dfrac{1 \text{ mol}}{95.94 \text{ g}} = 0.5000 \text{ mol Mo}$

22. a. $0.00552 \text{ mol Ca} \times \dfrac{40.08 \text{ g}}{1 \text{ mol}} = 0.221 \text{ g Ca}$

    b. $6.25 \text{ millimol B} \times \dfrac{1 \text{ mol}}{10^3 \text{ millmol}} \times \dfrac{10.81 \text{ g}}{1 \text{ mol}} = 0.0676 \text{ g B}$

    c. $135 \text{ mol Al} \times \dfrac{26.98 \text{ g}}{1 \text{ mol}} = 3.64 \times 10^3 \text{ g Al}$

    d. $1.34 \times 10^{-7} \text{ mol Ba} \times \dfrac{137.3 \text{ g}}{1 \text{ mol}} = 1.84 \times 10^{-5} \text{ g Ba}$

e. $2.79 \text{ mol P} \times \dfrac{30.97 \text{ g}}{1 \text{ mol}} = 86.4 \text{ g P}$

f. $0.0000997 \text{ mol As} \times \dfrac{74.92 \text{ g}}{1 \text{ mol}} = 7.47 \times 10^{-3} \text{ g As}$

24. a. $125 \text{ Fe atoms} \times \dfrac{55.85 \text{ g Fe}}{6.022 \times 10^{23} \text{ Fe atoms}} = 1.16 \times 10^{-20} \text{ g}$

b. $125 \text{ Fe atoms} \times \dfrac{55.85 \text{ amu}}{1 \text{ Fe atom}} = 6.98 \times 10^{3} \text{ amu}$

c. $125 \text{ g Fe} \times \dfrac{1 \text{ mol Fe}}{55.85 \text{ g Fe}} = 2.24 \text{ mol Fe}$

d. $125 \text{ mol Fe} \times \dfrac{55.85 \text{ g Fe}}{1 \text{ mol Fe}} = 6.98 \times 10^{3} \text{ g Fe}$

e. $125 \text{ g Fe} \times \dfrac{6.022 \times 10^{23} \text{ Fe atoms}}{55.85 \text{ g Fe}} = 1.35 \times 10^{24} \text{ Fe atoms}$

f. $125 \text{ mol Fe} \times \dfrac{6.022 \times 10^{23} \text{ Fe atoms}}{1 \text{ mol Fe}} = 7.53 \times 10^{25} \text{ Fe atoms}$

26. The molar mass is calculated by summing the individual atomic masses of the atoms in the formula.

28. a. $KHCO_3$ potassium hydrogen carbonate, potassium bicarbonate

    mass of 1 mol K = 39.10 g

    mass of 1 mol H = 1.008 g

    mass of 1 mol C = 12.01 g

    mass of 3 mol O = 3(16.00 g) = 48.00 g

    molar mass of $KHCO_3$ = (39.10 + 1.008 + 12.01 + 48.00) = 100.12 g

    b. Hg_2Cl_2 mercurous chloride, mercury(I) chloride

    mass of 2 mol Hg = 2(200.6 g) = 401.2 g

    mass of 2 mol Cl = 2(35.45 g) = 70.90 g

    molar mass of Hg_2Cl_2 = (401.2 g + 70.90 g) = 472.1 g

    c. H_2O_2 hydrogen peroxide

    mass of 2 mol H = 2(1.008 g) = 2.016 g

    mass of 2 mol O = 2(16.00 g) = 32.00 g

    molar mass of H_2O_2 = (2.016 g + 32.00 g) = 34.02 g

    d. $BeCl_2$ beryllium chloride

    mass of 1 mol Be = 9.012 g

mass of 2 mol Cl = 2(35.45 g) = 70.90 g

molar mass of $BeCl_2$ = (9.012 g + 70.90 g) = 79.91 g

e. $Al_2(SO_4)_3$ aluminum sulfate

mass of 2 mol Al = 2(26.98 g) = 53.96 g

mass of 3 mol S = 3(32.07 g) = 96.21 g

mass of 12 mol O = 12(16.00 g) = 192.0 g

molar mass of $Al_2(SO_4)_3$ = (53.96 g + 96.21 g + 192.0 g) = 342.2 g

f. $KClO_3$ potassium chlorate

mass of 1 mol K = 39.10 g

mass of 1 mol Cl = 35.45 g

mass of 3 mol O = 3(16.00 g) = 48.00 g

molar mass of $KClO_3$ = 122.55 g

30. a. $LiClO_4$

mass of 1 mol Li = 6.941 g

mass of 1 mol Cl = 35.45 g

mass of 4 mol O = 4(16.00 g) = 64.00 g

molar mass of $LiClO_4$ = (6.941 g + 35.45 g + 64.00 g) = 106.39 g

b. $NaHSO_4$

mass of 1 mol Na = 22.99 g

mass of 1 mol H = 1.008 g

mass of 1 mol S = 32.07 g = 32.07 g

mass of 4 mol O = 4(16.00 g) = 64.00 g

molar mass of $NaHSO_4$ = (22.99 g + 1.008 g + 32.07 g + 64.00 g) = 120.07 g

c. $MgCO_3$

mass of 1 mol Mg = 24.31 g

mass of 1 mol C = 12.01 g

mass of 3 mol O = 3(16.00 g) = 48.00 g

molar mass of $MgCO_3$ = (24.31 g + 12.01 g + 48.00 g) = 84.32 g

d. $AlBr_3$

mass of 1 mol Al = 26.98 g

mass of 3 mol Br = 3(79.90 g) = 239.7 g

molar mass of $AlBr_3$ = (26.98 g + 239.7 g) = 266.7 g

e. Cr_2S_3

mass of 2 mol Cr = 2(52.00 g) = 104.0 g

mass of 3 mol S = 3(32.07 g) = 96.21 g

molar mass of Cr_2S_3 = (104.0 + 96.21 g) = 200.2 g

32. a. molar mass Al_2O_3 = 101.96 g

$$47.2 \text{ g} \times \frac{1 \text{ mol}}{101.96 \text{ g}} = 0.463 \text{ mol}$$

b. molar mass KBr = 119.00 g

$$1.34 \text{ kg} \times \frac{1000 \text{ g}}{1 \text{ kg}} \times \frac{1 \text{ mol}}{119.00 \text{ g}} = 11.3 \text{ mol}$$

c. molar mass Ge = 72.59 g

$$521 \text{ mg} \times \frac{1 \text{ g}}{1000 \text{ mg}} \times \frac{1 \text{ mol}}{72.59 \text{ g}} = 7.18 \times 10^{-3} \text{ mol}$$

d. molar mass of U = 238.0 g

$$56.2 \text{ μg} \times \frac{1 \text{ g}}{10^6 \text{ μg}} \times \frac{1 \text{ mol}}{238.0 \text{ g}} = 2.36 \times 10^{-7} \text{ mol}$$

e. molar mass of $NaC_2H_3O_2$ = 82.03 g

$$29.7 \text{ g} \times \frac{1 \text{ mol}}{82.03 \text{ g}} = 1.69 \text{ mol} = 0.362 \text{ mol}$$

f. molar mass of SO_3 = 80.07 g

$$1.03 \text{ g} \times \frac{1 \text{ mol}}{80.07 \text{ g}} = 0.0129 \text{ mol}$$

34. a. molar mass of Li_2CO_3 = 73.89 g

$$1.95 \times 10^{-3} \text{ g} \times \frac{1 \text{ mol}}{73.89 \text{ g}} = 2.64 \times 10^{-5} \text{ mol}$$

b. molar mass of $CaCl_2$ = 110.98 g

$$4.23 \text{ kg} \times \frac{1000 \text{ g}}{1 \text{ kg}} \times \frac{1 \text{ mol}}{110.98 \text{ g}} = 38.1 \text{ mol}$$

c. molar mass of $SrCl_2$ = 158.52 g

$$1.23 \text{ mg} \times \frac{1 \text{ g}}{1000 \text{ mg}} \times \frac{1 \text{ mol}}{158.52 \text{ g}} = 7.76 \times 10^{-6} \text{ mol}$$

d. molar mass of $CaSO_4$ = 136.15 g

$$4.75 \text{ g} \times \frac{1 \text{ mol}}{136.15 \text{ g}} = 3.49 \times 10^{-2} \text{ mol}$$

e.   molar mass of NO_2 = 46.01 g

$$96.2 \text{ mg} \times \frac{1 \text{ g}}{1000 \text{ mg}} \times \frac{1 \text{ mol}}{46.01 \text{ g}} = 2.09 \times 10^{-3} \text{ mol}$$

f.   molar mass of Hg_2Cl_2 = 472.1 g

$$12.7 \text{ g} \times \frac{1 \text{ mol}}{472.1 \text{ g}} = 0.0269 \text{ mol}$$

36.   a.   molar mass of H_2S = 34.09 g

$$1.21 \text{ mol} \times \frac{34.09 \text{ g}}{1 \text{ mol}} = 41.2 \text{ g}$$

b.   molar mass of Li_2S = 45.95 g

$$4.22 \times 10^{-3} \text{ mol} \times \frac{45.95 \text{ g}}{1 \text{ mol}} = 0.194 \text{ g}$$

c.   molar mass of $FeCl_3$ = 162.2 g

$$224 \text{ mol} \times \frac{162.2 \text{ g}}{1 \text{ mol}} = 3.63 \times 10^4 \text{ g}$$

d.   molar mass of Na_2CO_3 = 105.99 g

$$7.29 \text{ millmol} \times \frac{1 \text{ mol}}{10^3 \text{ millimol}} \times \frac{105.99 \text{ g}}{1 \text{ mol}} = 0.773 \text{ g}$$

e.   molar mass of $NaC_2H_3O_2$ = 82.03 g

$$8.14 \times 10^3 \text{ mol} \times \frac{82.03 \text{ g}}{1 \text{ mol}} = 6.68 \times 10^5 \text{ g}$$

f.   molar mass of PH_3 = 33.99 g

$$0.00793 \text{ mol} \times \frac{33.99 \text{ g}}{1 \text{ mol}} = 0.270 \text{ g}$$

38.   a.   molar mass C_6H_6 = 78.11 g

$$0.994 \text{ mol} \times \frac{78.11 \text{ g}}{1 \text{ mol}} = 77.6 \text{ g}$$

b.   molar mass CaH_2 = 42.10 g

$$4.21 \text{ mol} \times \frac{42.10 \text{ g}}{1 \text{ mol}} = 177 \text{ g}$$

c.   molar mass H_2O_2 = 34.02 g

$$1.79 \times 10^{-4} \text{ mol} \times \frac{34.02 \text{ g}}{1 \text{ mol}} = 6.09 \times 10^{-3} \text{ g}$$

      d.   molar mass $C_6H_{12}O_6$ = 180.16 g

$$1.22 \text{ mmol} \times \frac{1 \text{ mol}}{10^3 \text{ mmol}} \times \frac{105.99 \text{ g}}{1 \text{ mol}} = 0.220 \text{ g}$$

      e.   molar mass Sn = 118.7 g

$$10.6 \text{ mol} \times \frac{118.7 \text{ g}}{1 \text{ mol}} = 1.26 \times 10^3 \text{ g}$$

      f.   molar mass SrF_2 = 125.62 g

$$0.000301 \text{ mol} \times \frac{125.62 \text{ g}}{1 \text{ mol}} = 0.0378 \text{ g}$$

40.   a. $6.37 \text{ mol CO} \times \dfrac{6.022 \times 10^{23} \text{ molecules}}{1 \text{ mol}} = 3.84 \times 10^{24} \text{ molecules CO}$

      b.   molar mass of CO = 28.01 g

$$6.37 \text{ g} \times \frac{6.022 \times 10^{23} \text{ molecules}}{28.01 \text{ g}} = 1.37 \times 10^{23} \text{ molecules CO}$$

      c.   molar mass of H_2O = 18.02 g

$$2.62 \times 10^{-6} \text{ g} \times \frac{6.022 \times 10^{23} \text{ molecules}}{18.02 \text{ g}} = 8.76 \times 10^{16} \text{ molecules } H_2O$$

      d. $2.62 \times 10^{-6} \text{ g} \times \dfrac{6.022 \times 10^{23} \text{ molecules}}{1 \text{ mol}} = 1.58 \times 10^{18} \text{ molec. } H_2O$

      e.   molar mass of C_6H_6 = 78.11 g

$$5.23 \text{ g} \times \frac{6.022 \times 10^{23} \text{ molecules}}{78.11 \text{ g}} = 4.03 \times 10^{22} \text{ molecules } C_6H_6$$

42.   a.   molar mass of Na_2SO_4 = 142.1 g

$$2.01 \text{ g } Na_2SO_4 \times \frac{1 \text{ mol } Na_2SO_4}{142.1 \text{ g}} \times \frac{1 \text{ mol S}}{1 \text{ mol } Na_2SO_4} = 0.0141 \text{ mol S}$$

      b.   molar mass of Na_2SO_3 = 126.1 g

$$2.01 \text{ g } Na_2SO_3 \times \frac{1 \text{ mol } Na_2SO_3}{126.1 \text{ g}} \times \frac{1 \text{ mol S}}{1 \text{ mol } Na_2SO_3} = 0.0159 \text{ mol S}$$

      c.   molar mass of Na_2S = 78.05 g

$$2.01 \text{ g } Na_2S \times \frac{1 \text{ mol } Na_2S}{78.05 \text{ g}} \times \frac{1 \text{ mol S}}{1 \text{ mol } Na_2S} = 0.0258 \text{ mol S}$$

      d.   molar mass of $Na_2S_2O_3$ = 158.1 g

$$2.01 \text{ g } Na_2S_2O_3 \times \frac{1 \text{ mol } Na_2S_2O_3}{158.1 \text{ g}} \times \frac{1 \text{ mol S}}{1 \text{ mol } Na_2S} = 0.0127 \text{ mol S}$$

44.   less than

46.   a.   mass of Zn present = 65.38 g

mass of O present = 16.00 g

molar mass of ZnO = 81.38 g

$$\%Zn = \frac{65.38 \text{ g Zn}}{81.38 \text{ g}} \times 100 = 80.34\% \text{ Zn}$$

$$\%O = \frac{16.00 \text{ g O}}{81.38 \text{ g}} \times 100 = 19.66\% \text{ O}$$

b.   mass of Na present = 2(22.99 g) = 45.98 g

mass of S present = 32.07 g

molar mass of Na_2S = 78.05 g

$$\%Na = \frac{45.98 \text{ g Na}}{78.05 \text{ g}} \times 100 = 58.91\% \text{ Na}$$

$$\%S = \frac{32.07 \text{ g S}}{78.05 \text{ g}} \times 100 = 41.09\% \text{ S}$$

c.   mass of Mg present = 24.31 g

mass of O present = 2(16.00 g) = 32.00 g

mass of H present = 2(1.008 g) = 2.016 g

molar mass of $Mg(OH)_2$ = 58.33 g

$$\%Mg = \frac{24.31 \text{ g Mg}}{58.33 \text{ g}} \times 100 = 41.68\% \text{ Mg}$$

$$\%O = \frac{32.00 \text{ g O}}{58.33 \text{ g}} \times 100 = 54.86\% \text{ O}$$

$$\%H = \frac{2.016 \text{ g H}}{58.33 \text{ g}} \times 100 = 3.456\% \text{ H}$$

d.   mass of H present = 2(1.008 g) = 2.016 g

mass of O present = 2(16.00 g) = 32.00 g

molar mass of H_2O_2 = 34.02 g

$$\%H = \frac{2.016 \text{ g H}}{34.02 \text{ g}} \times 100 = 5.926\% \text{ H}$$

$$\%O = \frac{32.00 \text{ g O}}{34.02 \text{ g}} \times 100 = 94.06\% \text{ O}$$

e. mass of Ca present = 40.08 g

mass of H present = 2(1.008 g) = 2.016 g

molar mass of CaH_2 = 42.10 g

$$\%Ca = \frac{40.08 \text{ g Ca}}{42.10 \text{ g}} \times 100 = 95.20\% \text{ Ca}$$

$$\%H = \frac{2.016 \text{ g H}}{42.10 \text{ g}} \times 100 = 4.789\% \text{ H}$$

f. mass of K present = 2(39.10 g) = 78.20 g

mass of O present = 16.00 g

molar mass of K_2O = 94.20 g

$$\%K = \frac{78.20 \text{ g K}}{94.20 \text{ g}} \times 100 = 83.01\% \text{ K}$$

$$\%O = \frac{16.00 \text{ g O}}{94.20 \text{ g}} \times 100 = 16.99\% \text{ O}$$

48. a. molar mass of BaO_2 = 169.3 g

$$\% \text{ Ba} = \frac{137.3 \text{ g Ba}}{169.3 \text{ g}} \times 100 = 81.10\% \text{ Ba}$$

b. molar mass of BaO = 153.3 g

$$\% \text{ Ba} = \frac{137.3 \text{ g Ba}}{153.3 \text{ g}} \times 100 = 89.56\% \text{ Ba}$$

c. molar mass of $CoBr_2$ = 218.73 g

$$\% \text{ Co} = \frac{58.93 \text{ g Co}}{218.73 \text{ g}} \times 100 = 26.94\% \text{ Co}$$

d. molar mass of $CoBr_3$ = 298.63 g

$$\% \text{ Co} = \frac{58.93 \text{ g Co}}{298.63 \text{ g}} \times 100 = 19.73\% \text{ Co}$$

e. molar mass of $SnCl_2$ = 189.60 g

$$\% \text{ Sn} = \frac{118.7 \text{ g Sn}}{189.60 \text{ g}} \times 100 = 62.61\% \text{ Sn}$$

f. molar mass of $SnCl_4$ = 260.50 g

$$\% \text{ Sn} = \frac{118.7 \text{ g Sn}}{260.50 \text{ g}} \times 100 = 45.57\% \text{ Sn}$$

g.   molar mass of LiH = 7.949 g

$$\% \, Li = \frac{6.941 \text{ g Li}}{7.949 \text{ g}} \times 100 = 87.32\% \, Li$$

h.   molar mass of AlH$_3$ = 30.00 g

$$\% \, Al = \frac{26.98 \text{ g Al}}{30.00 \text{ g}} \times 100 = 89.93\% \, Al$$

50.   a.   molar mass of ICl = 162.35 g

$$\%I = \frac{126.9 \text{ g I}}{162.35 \text{ g}} \times 100 = 78.16\% \, I$$

b.   molar mass of N$_2$O = 44.02 g

$$\%N = \frac{28.02 \text{ g N}}{44.02 \text{ g}} \times 100 = 63.65\% \, N$$

c.   molar mass of NO = 30.01 g

$$\%N = \frac{14.01 \text{ g N}}{30.01 \text{ g}} \times 100 = 46.68\% \, N$$

d.   molar mass of HgCl$_2$ = 271.5 g

$$\%Hg = \frac{200.6 \text{ g Hg}}{271.5 \text{ g}} \times 100 = 73.89\% \, Hg$$

e.   molar mass of Hg$_2$Cl$_2$ = 472.1 g

$$\%Hg = \frac{401.2 \text{ g Hg}}{472.1 \text{ g}} \times 100 = 84.98\% \, Hg$$

f.   molar mass of SF$_6$ = 146.07 g

$$\%S = \frac{32.07 \text{ g S}}{146.07 \text{ g}} \times 100 = 21.96\% \, S$$

g.   molar mass of XeF$_2$ = 169.3 g

$$\%Xe = \frac{131.3 \text{ g Xe}}{169.3 \text{ g}} \times 100 = 77.55\% \, Xe$$

h.   molar mass of MnO$_2$ = 86.94 g

$$\%Mn = \frac{54.94 \text{ g Mn}}{86.94 \text{ g}} \times 100 = 63.19\% \, Mn$$

52.   a.   molar mass of (NH$_4$)$_2$S = 68.15 g; molar mass of S^{2-} ion = 32.07 g

$$\% \, S^{2-} = \frac{32.07 \text{ g S}^{2-}}{68.15 \text{ g NH}_4\text{S}} \times 100 = 47.06\% \, S^{2-}$$

b.   molar mass of $CaCl_2$ = 110.98 g; molar mass of Cl^- = 35.45 g

$$\% \ Cl^- = \frac{70.90 \ g \ Cl^-}{110.98 \ g \ CaCl_2} \times 100 = 63.89\% \ Cl^-$$

c.   molar mass of BaO = 153.3 g; molar mass of O^{2-} ion = 16.00 g

$$\% \ O^{2-} = \frac{16.00 \ g \ O^{2-}}{153.3 \ g \ BaO} \times 100 = 10.44\% \ O^{2-}$$

d.   molar mass of $NiSO_4$ = 154.76 g; molar mass of SO_4^{2-} ion = 96.07 g

$$\% \ SO_4^{2-} = \frac{96.07 \ g \ SO_4^{2-}}{154.76 \ g \ NiSO_4} \times 100 = 62.08\% \ SO_4^{2-}$$

54.   The empirical formula indicates the smallest whole number ratio of the number and type of atoms present in a molecule. For example, NO_2 and N_2O_4 both have two oxygen atoms for every nitrogen atom and therefore have the same empirical formula

56.   a.   yes (each of these has empirical formula CH)

b.   no (the number of hydrogen atoms is wrong)

c.   yes (both have empirical formula NO_2)

d.   no (the number of hydrogen and oxygen atoms is wrong)

58.   Assume we have 100.0 g of the compound so that the percentages become masses.

$$11.64 \ g \ N \times \frac{1 \ mol}{14.01 \ g} = 0.8308 \ mol \ N$$

$$88.36 \ g \ Cl \times \frac{1 \ mol}{35.45 \ g} = 2.493 \ mol \ Cl$$

Dividing both of these numbers of moles by the smaller number of moles gives

$$\frac{0.8308 \ mol \ N}{0.8308} = 1.000 \ mol \ N$$

$$\frac{2.493 \ mol \ Cl}{0.8308 \ mol} = 3.001 \ mol \ Cl$$

The empirical formula is NCl_3.

60.   Assume we have 100.0 g of the compound, so that the percentages become masses.

$$78.14 \ g \ B \times \frac{1 \ mol}{10.81 \ g} = 7.228 \ mol \ B$$

$$21.86 \ g \ H \times \frac{1 \ mol}{1.008 \ g} = 21.69 \ mol \ H$$

Dividing each number of moles by the smaller number of moles gives

$$\frac{7.228 \text{ mol B}}{7.228 \text{ mol}} = 1.000 \text{ mol B}$$

$$\frac{21.69 \text{ mol H}}{7.228 \text{ mol}} = 3.000 \text{ mol H}$$

The empirical formula is BH_3.

62. Consider 100.0 g of the compound so that percentages become masses.

$$45.56 \text{ g Sn} \times \frac{1 \text{ mol}}{118.7 \text{ g}} = 0.3838 \text{ mol Sn}$$

$$54.43 \text{ g Cl} \times \frac{1 \text{ mol}}{35.45 \text{ g}} = 1.535 \text{ mol Cl}$$

Dividing each number of moles by the smaller number of moles gives

$$\frac{0.3838 \text{ mol Sn}}{0.3838 \text{ mol}} = 1.000 \text{ mol Sn}$$

$$\frac{1.535 \text{ mol Cl}}{0.3838 \text{ mol}} = 3.999 \text{ mol Cl}$$

The empirical formula is $SnCl_4$.

64. Consider 100.0 g of the compound.

$$55.06 \text{ g Co} \times \frac{1 \text{ mol}}{58.93 \text{ g}} = 0.9343 \text{ mol Co}$$

If the sulfide of cobalt is 55.06% Co, then it is 44.94% S by mass.

$$44.94 \text{ g S} \times \frac{1 \text{ mol}}{32.07 \text{ g}} = 1.401 \text{ mol S}$$

Dividing each number of moles by the smaller (0.9343 mol Co) gives

$$\frac{0.09343 \text{ mol Co}}{0.9343} = 1.000 \text{ mol Co}$$

$$\frac{1.401 \text{ mol S}}{0.9343 \text{ mol}} = 1.500 \text{ mol S}$$

Multiplying by two, to convert to whole numbers of moles, gives the empirical formula for the compound as Co_2S_3.

66.
$$2.50 \text{ g Al} \times \frac{1 \text{ mol}}{26.98 \text{ g}} = 0.09266 \text{ mol Al}$$

$$5.28 \text{ g F} \times \frac{1 \text{ mol}}{19.00 \text{ g}} = 0.2779 \text{ mol F}$$

Dividing each number of moles by the smaller number of moles gives

$$\frac{0.09266 \text{ mol Al}}{0.09266 \text{ mol}} = 1.000 \text{ mol Al}$$

$$\frac{0.2779 \text{ mol F}}{0.09266 \text{ mol}} = 2.999 \text{ mol F}$$

The empirical formula is just AlF_3. Note the similarity between this problem and question 65: they differ in the way the data is given. In question 65, you were given the mass of the product, and first had to calculate how much fluorine had reacted.

68.   Consider 100.0 g of the compound so that percentages become masses.

$$46.46 \text{ g Li} \times \frac{1 \text{ mol}}{6.941 \text{ g}} = 6.694 \text{ mol Li}$$

$$53.54 \text{ g O} \times \frac{1 \text{ mol}}{16.00 \text{ g}} = 3.346 \text{ mol O}$$

Dividing each number of moles by the smaller number of moles gives

$$\frac{6.694 \text{ mol Li}}{3.346 \text{ mol}} = 2.001 \text{ mol Li}$$

$$\frac{3.346 \text{ mol O}}{3.346 \text{ mol}} = 1.000 \text{ mol O}$$

The empirical formula is Li_2O

70.   Consider 100.0 g of the compound.

$$59.78 \text{ g Li} \times \frac{1 \text{ mol}}{6.941 \text{ g}} = 8.613 \text{ mol Li}$$

$$40.22 \text{ g N} \times \frac{1 \text{ mol}}{14.01 \text{ g}} = 2.871 \text{ mol N}$$

Dividing each number of moles by the smaller number of moles (2.871 mol N) gives

$$\frac{8.613 \text{ mol Li}}{2.871 \text{ mol}} = 3.000 \text{ mol Li}$$

$$\frac{2.871 \text{ mol N}}{2.871 \text{ mol}} = 1.000 \text{ mol N}$$

The empirical formula is Li_3N.

72.   Consider 100.0 g of the compound so that percentages become masses.

$$71.06 \text{ g Co} \times \frac{1 \text{ mol}}{58.93 \text{ g}} = 1.206 \text{ mol Co}$$

$$28.94 \text{ g O} \times \frac{1 \text{ mol}}{16.00 \text{ g}} = 1.809 \text{ mol O}$$

Dividing each number of moles by the smaller number of moles gives

$$\frac{1.206 \text{ mol Co}}{1.206 \text{ mol}} = 1.000 \text{ mol Co}$$

$$\frac{1.809 \text{ mol O}}{1.206 \text{ mol}} = 1.500 \text{ mol O}$$

Multiplying these relative numbers of moles by 2 to give whole numbers gives the empirical formula as Co_2O_3

74.   Compound 1: Assume 100.0 g of the compound.

$$22.55 \text{ g P} \times \frac{1 \text{ mol}}{30.97 \text{ g}} = 0.7281 \text{ mol P}$$

$$77.45 \text{ g Cl} \times \frac{1 \text{ mol}}{35.45 \text{ g}} = 2.185 \text{ mol Cl}$$

Dividing each number of moles by the smaller (0.7281 mol P) indicates that the formula of Compound 1 is PCl_3.

Compound 2: Assume 100.0 g of the compound.

$$14.87 \text{ g P} \times \frac{1 \text{ mol}}{30.97 \text{ g}} = 0.4801 \text{ mol P}$$

$$85.13 \text{ g Cl} \times \frac{1 \text{ mol}}{35.45 \text{ g}} = 2.401 \text{ mol Cl}$$

Dividing each number of moles by the smaller (0.4801 mol P) indicates that the formula of Compound 2 is PCl_5.

76.   If only the empirical formula is known, the molar mass of the substance must be determined before the molecular formula can be calculated.

78.   empirical formula mass of CH = 13 g

$$n = \frac{\text{molar mass}}{\text{empirical formula mass}} = \frac{78 \text{ g}}{13 \text{ g}} = 6$$

The molecular formula is $(CH)_6$ or C_6H_6.

80.   empirical formula mass of C_2H_5O = 46 g

$$n = \frac{\text{molar mass}}{\text{empirical formula mass}} = \frac{90 \text{ g}}{46 \text{ g}} = \sim 2$$

molecular formula is $(C_2H_5O)_2 = C_4H_{10}O_2$

82.   For NO_2:   molar mass = 14.01 + 2(16.00) = 46.01 g

$$\%N = \frac{14.01 \text{ g N}}{46.01 \text{ g}} \times 100 = 30.45 \text{ \%N}$$

$$\%O = \frac{2(16.00 \text{ g O})}{46.01 \text{ g}} \times 100 = 69.55 \ \%O$$

For N_2O_4: molar mass $= 2(14.01 \text{ g}) + 4(16.00 \text{ g}) = 92.02 \text{ g}$

$$\%N = \frac{2(14.01 \text{ g N})}{92.02 \text{ g}} \times 100 = 30.45 \ \%N$$

$$\%O = \frac{4(16.00 \text{ g O})}{92.02 \text{ g}} \times 100 = 69.55 \ \%O$$

84. | 5.00 g Al | 0.185 mol | 1.12×10^{23} atoms |
        |---|---|---|
        | 0.140 g Fe | 0.00250 mol | 1.51×10^{21} atoms |
        | 2.7×10^2 g Cu | 4.3 mol | 2.6×10^{24} atoms |
        | 0.00250 g Mg | 1.03×10^{-4} mol | 6.19×10^{19} atoms |
        | 0.062 g Na | 2.7×10^{-3} mol | 1.6×10^{21} atoms |
        | 3.95×10^{-18} g U | 1.66×10^{-20} mol | 1.00×10^{4} atoms |

86.   mass of 2 mol X $= 2(41.2 \text{ g}) = 82.4 \text{ g}$

mass of 1 mol Y $= 57.7 \text{ g} = 57.7 \text{ g}$

mass of 3 mol Z $= 3(63.9 \text{ g}) = 191.7 \text{ g}$

molar mass of $X_2YZ_3 = 331.8 \text{ g}$

$$\%X = \frac{82.4 \text{ g}}{331.8 \text{ g}} \times 100 = 24.8 \ \%X$$

$$\% Y = \frac{57.7 \text{ g}}{331.8 \text{ g}} \times 100 = 17.4\% \ Y$$

$$\% Z = \frac{191.7 \text{ g}}{331.8 \text{ g}} \times 100 = 57.8\% \ Z$$

If the molecular formula were actually $X_4Y_2Z_6$, the percentage composition would be the same, and the *relative* mass of each element present would not change. The molecular formula is always a whole number multiple of the empirical formula.

88.   For the first compound (*restricted* amount of oxygen)

$$2.118 \text{ g Cu} \times \frac{1 \text{ mol}}{63.55 \text{ g}} = 0.03333 \text{ mol Cu}$$

$$0.2666 \text{ g O} \times \frac{1 \text{ mol}}{16.00 \text{ g}} = 0.01666 \text{ mol O}$$

Since the number of moles of Cu (0.03333 mol) is twice the number of moles of O (0.01666 mol), the empirical formula is Cu_2O.

For the second compound (stream of pure oxygen)

$$2.118 \text{ g Cu} \times \frac{1 \text{ mol}}{63.55 \text{ g}} = 0.03333 \text{ mol Cu}$$

$$0.5332 \text{ g O} \times \frac{1 \text{ mol}}{16.00 \text{ g}} = 0.03333 \text{ mol O}$$

Since the numbers of moles are the same, the empirical formula is CuO.

90.   a.   molar mass H_2O = 18.02 g

$$4.21 \text{ g} \times \frac{1 \text{ mol}}{18.02 \text{ g}} \times \frac{6.022 \times 10^{23} \text{ molecules}}{1 \text{ mol}} = 1.41 \times 10^{23} \text{ molecules}$$

The sample contains 1.41×10^{23} oxygen atoms and $2(1.41 \times 10^{23}) = 2.82 \times 10^{23}$ hydrogen atoms.

   b.   molar mass CO_2 = 44.01 g

$$6.81 \text{ g} \times \frac{1 \text{ mol}}{44.01 \text{ g}} \times \frac{6.022 \times 10^{23} \text{ molecules}}{1 \text{ mol}} = 9.32 \times 10^{22} \text{ molecules}$$

The sample contains 9.32×10^{22} carbon atoms and $2(9.32 \times 10^{22}) = 1.86 \times 10^{23}$ oxygen atoms.

   c.   molar mass C_6H_6 = 78.11 g

$$0.000221 \text{ g} \times \frac{1 \text{ mol}}{78.11 \text{ g}} \times \frac{6.022 \times 10^{23} \text{ molecules}}{1 \text{ mol}} = 1.70 \times 10^{18} \text{ molec.}$$

The sample contains $6(1.70 \times 10^{18}) = 1.02 \times 10^{19}$ atoms of each element.

   d.

$$2.26 \text{ mol} \times \frac{6.022 \times 10^{23} \text{ molecules}}{1 \text{ mol}} = 1.36 \times 10^{24} \text{ molecules}$$

atoms C = $12(1.36 \times 10^{24}) = 1.63 \times 10^{25}$ atoms

atoms H = $22(1.36 \times 10^{24}) = 2.99 \times 10^{25}$ atoms

atoms O = $11(1.36 \times 10^{24}) = 1.50 \times 10^{25}$ atoms

92.   a.   molar mass of C_3O_2 = 3(12.01 g) + 2(16.00 g) = 68.03 g

$$\% \text{ C} = \frac{36.03 \text{ g C}}{68.03 \text{ g}} \times 100 = 52.96\% \text{ C}$$

$$7.819 \text{ g } C_3O_2 \times \frac{52.96 \text{ g C}}{100.0 \text{ g } C_3O_2} = 4.141 \text{ g C}$$

$$4.141 \text{ g C} \times \frac{6.022 \times 10^{23} \text{ molecules}}{12.01 \text{ g C}} = 2.076 \times 10^{23} \text{ C atoms}$$

   b.   molar mass of CO = 12.01 g + 16.00 g = 28.01 g

$$\% \text{ C} = \frac{12.01 \text{ g C}}{28.01 \text{ g}} \times 100 = 42.88\% \text{ C}$$

$$1.53 \times 10^{21} \text{ molecules CO} \times \frac{1 \text{ C atom}}{1 \text{ molecule CO}} = 1.53 \times 10^{21} \text{ C atoms}$$

$$1.53 \times 10^{21} \text{ C atoms} \times \frac{12.01 \text{ g C}}{6.022 \times 10^{23} \text{ C atoms}} = 0.0305 \text{ g C}$$

c.   molar mass of C_6H_6O = 6(12.01 g) + 6(1.008 g) + 16.00 g = 94.11 g

$$\% \text{ C} = \frac{72.06 \text{ g C}}{94.11 \text{ g}} \times 100 = 76.57\% \text{ C}$$

$$0.200 \text{ mol } C_6H_6O \times \frac{6 \text{ mol C}}{1 \text{ mol } C_6H_6O} = 1.20 \text{ mol C}$$

$$1.20 \text{ mol C} \times \frac{12.01 \text{ g}}{1 \text{ mol}} = 14.4 \text{ g C}$$

$$14.4 \text{ g C} \times \frac{6.022 \times 10^{23} \text{ C atoms}}{12.01 \text{ g C}} = 7.22 \times 10^{23} \text{ C atoms}$$

94. $2.24 \text{ g Co} \times \dfrac{55.85 \text{ g Fe}}{58.93 \text{ g Co}} = 2.12 \text{ g Fe}$

96. $5.00 \text{ g Te} \times \dfrac{200.6 \text{ g Hg}}{127.6 \text{ g Te}} = 7.86 \text{ g Hg}$

98. $153.8 \text{ g CCl}_4 = 6.022 \times 10^{23} \text{ molecules CCl}_4$

$$1 \text{ molecule} \times \frac{153.8 \text{ g CCl}_4}{6.022 \times 10^{23} \text{ molecules}} = 2.554 \times 10^{-22} \text{ g}$$

100.   a.   molar mass of $C_2H_5O_2N$ = 2(12.01 g) + 5(1.008 g) + 2(16.00 g) + 14.01 g = 75.07 g

$$5.000 \text{ g} \times \frac{14.01 \text{ g N}}{75.07 \text{ g}} = 0.9331 \text{ g N}$$

b.   molar mass of Mg_3N_2 = 3(24.31 g) + 2(14.01 g) = 100.95 g

$$5.000 \text{ g} \times \frac{28.02 \text{ g N}}{100.95 \text{ g}} = 1.388 \text{ g N}$$

c.   molar mass of $Ca(NO_3)_2$ = 40.08 g + 2(14.01 g) + 6(16.00 g) = 164.10 g

$$5.000 \text{ g} \times \frac{28.02 \text{ g N}}{164.10 \text{ g}} = 0.8537 \text{ g N}$$

d.   molar mass of N_2O_4 = 2(14.01 g) + 4(16.00 g) = 92.02 g

$$5.000 \text{ g} \times \frac{28.02 \text{ g N}}{92.02 \text{ g}} = 1.522 \text{ g N}$$

102. Consider 100.0 g of the compound.

$$16.39 \text{ g Mg} \times \frac{1 \text{ mol}}{24.31 \text{ g}} = 0.6742 \text{ mol Mg}$$

$$18.89 \text{ g N} \times \frac{1 \text{ mol}}{14.01 \text{ g}} = 1.348 \text{ mol N}$$

$$64.72 \text{ g O} \times \frac{1 \text{ mol}}{16.00 \text{ g}} = 4.045 \text{ mol O}$$

Dividing each number of moles by the smallest number of moles

$$\frac{0.6742 \text{ mol Mg}}{0.6742 \text{ mol}} = 1.000 \text{ mol Mg}$$

$$\frac{1.348 \text{ mol N}}{0.6742 \text{ mol}} = 1.999 \text{ mol N}$$

$$\frac{4.045 \text{ mol O}}{0.6742 \text{ mol}} = 5.999 \text{ mol O}$$

The empirical formula is MgN_2O_6 [i.e., $Mg(NO_3)_2$].

104. We use the *average* mass because this average is a *weighted average* and takes into account both the masses and the relative abundances of the various isotopes.

106. $$1.98 \times 10^{13} \text{ amu} \times \frac{1 \text{ Na atom}}{22.99 \text{ amu}} = 8.61 \times 10^{11} \text{ Na atoms}$$

$$3.01 \times 10^{23} \text{ Na atoms} \times \frac{22.99 \text{ amu}}{1 \text{ Na atom}} = 6.92 \times 10^{24} \text{ amu}$$

108. a. $$5.0 \text{ mol K} \times \frac{39.10 \text{ g}}{1 \text{ mol}} = 195 \text{ g} = 2.0 \times 10^2 \text{ g K}$$

   b. $$0.000305 \text{ mol Hg} \times \frac{200.6 \text{ g}}{1 \text{ mol}} = 0.0612 \text{ g Hg}$$

   c. $$2.31 \times 10^{-5} \text{ mol Mn} \times \frac{54.94 \text{ g}}{1 \text{ mol}} = 1.27 \times 10^{-3} \text{ g Mn}$$

   d. $$10.5 \text{ mol P} \times \frac{30.97 \text{ g}}{1 \text{ mol}} = 325 \text{ g P}$$

   e. $$4.9 \times 10^4 \text{ mol Fe} \times \frac{55.85 \text{ g}}{1 \text{ mol}} = 2.7 \times 10^6 \text{ g Fe}$$

   f. $$125 \text{ mol Li} \times \frac{6.941 \text{ g}}{1 \text{ mol}} = 868 \text{ g Li}$$

   g. $$0.01205 \text{ mol F} \times \frac{19.00 \text{ g}}{1 \text{ mol}} = 0.2290 \text{ g F}$$

110.   a.   mass of 1 mol Fe = 1(55.85 g) = 55.85 g

mass of 1 mol S = 1(32.07 g) = 32.07 g

mass of 4 mol O = 4(16.00 g) = 64.00 g

molar mass of $FeSO_4$ = 151.92 g

b.   mass of 1 mol Hg = 1(200.6 g) = 200.6 g

mass of 2 mol I = 2(126.9 g) = 253.8 g

molar mass of HgI_2 =   454.4 g

c.   mass of 1 mol Sn = 1(118.7 g) = 118.7 g

mass of 2 mol O = 2(16.00 g) = 32.00 g

molar mass of SnO_2 = 150.7 g

d.   mass of 1 mol Co = 1(58.93 g) = 58.93 g

mass of 2 mol Cl = 2(35.45 g) = 70.90 g

molar mass of $CoCl_2$ = 129.83 g

e.   mass of 1 mol Cu = 1(63.55 g) = 63.55 g

mass of 2 mol N = 2(14.01 g) = 28.02 g

mass of 6 mol O = 6(16.00 g) = 96.00 g

molar mass of $Cu(NO_3)_2$ = 187.57 g

112.   a.   molar mass of $(NH_4)_2S$ = 68.15 g

$$21.2 \text{ g} \times \frac{1 \text{ mol}}{68.15 \text{ g}} = 0.311 \text{ mol } (NH_4)_2S$$

b.   molar mass of $Ca(NO_3)_2$ = 164.1 g

$$44.3 \text{ g} \times \frac{1 \text{ mol}}{164.1 \text{ g}} = 0.270 \text{ mol } Ca(NO_3)_2$$

c.   molar mass of Cl_2O = 86.9 g

$$4.35 \text{ g} \times \frac{1 \text{ mol}}{86.9 \text{ g}} = 0.0501 \text{ mol } Cl_2O$$

d.   1.0 lb = 454 g; molar mass of $FeCl_3$ = 162.2

$$454 \text{ g} \times \frac{1 \text{ mol}}{162.2 \text{ g}} = 2.8 \text{ mol } FeCl_3$$

e.   1.0 kg = 1.0×10^3 g;   molar mass of $FeCl_3$ = 162.2 g

$$1.0 \times 10^3 \text{ g} \times \frac{1 \text{ mol}}{162.2 \text{ g}} = 6.2 \text{ mol } FeCl_3$$

114.   a.   molar mass of $CuSO_4$ = 159.62 g

$$2.6 \times 10^{-2} \text{ mol} \times \frac{159.62 \text{ g}}{1 \text{ mol}} = 4.2 \text{ g } CuSO_4$$

        b.   molar mass of C_2F_4 = 100.0 g

$$3.05 \times 10^3 \text{ mol} \times \frac{100.0 \text{ g}}{1 \text{ mol}} = 3.05 \times 10^5 \text{ g } C_2F_4$$

        c.   7.83 mmol = 0.00783 mol; molar mass of C_5H_8 = 68.11 g

$$0.00783 \text{ mol} \times \frac{68.11 \text{ g}}{1 \text{ mol}} = 0.533 \text{ g } C_5H_8$$

        d.   molar mass of $BiCl_3$ = 315.3 g

$$6.30 \text{ mol} \times \frac{315.3 \text{ g}}{1 \text{ mol}} = 1.99 \times 10^3 \text{ g } BiCl_3$$

        e.   molar mass of $C_{12}H_{22}O_{11}$ = 342.3 g

$$12.2 \text{ mol} \times \frac{342.3 \text{ g}}{1 \text{ mol}} = 4.18 \times 10^3 \text{ g } C_{12}H_{22}O_{11}$$

116.   a.   molar mass of $C_6H_{12}O_6$ = 180.2 g

$$3.45 \text{ g} \times \frac{6.022 \times 10^{23} \text{ molecules}}{180.2 \text{ g}} = 1.15 \times 10^{22} \text{ molecules } C_6H_{12}O_6$$

        b. $3.45 \text{ mol} \times \frac{6.022 \times 10^{23} \text{ molecules}}{1 \text{ mol}} = 2.08 \times 10^{24} \text{ molecules } C_6H_{12}O_6$

        c.   molar mass of ICl_5 = 304.2 g

$$25.0 \text{ g} \times \frac{6.022 \times 10^{23} \text{ molecules}}{304.2 \text{ g}} = 4.95 \times 10^{22} \text{ molecules } ICl_5$$

        d.   molar mass of B_2H_6 = 27.67 g

$$1.00 \text{ g} \times \frac{6.022 \times 10^{23} \text{ molecules}}{27.67 \text{ g}} = 2.18 \times 10^{22} \text{ molecules } B_2H_6$$

        e.   1.05 mmol = 0.00105 mol

$$0.00105 \text{ mol} \times \frac{6.022 \times 10^{23} \text{ formula units}}{1 \text{ mol}} = 6.32 \times 10^{20} \text{ formula units}$$

118.   a.   mass of Ca present = 3(40.08 g) = 120.24 g

        mass of P present = 2(30.97 g) = 61.94 g

        mass of O present = 8(16.00 g) = 128.00 g

        molar mass of $Ca_3(PO_4)_2$ = 310.18 g

$$\% \text{ Ca} = \frac{120.24 \text{ g Ca}}{310.18 \text{ g}} \times 100 = 38.76\% \text{ Ca}$$

$$\% \text{ P} = \frac{61.94 \text{ g P}}{310.18 \text{ g}} \times 100 = 19.97\% \text{ P}$$

$$\% \text{ O} = \frac{128.00 \text{ g O}}{310.18 \text{ g}} \times 100 = 41.27\% \text{ O}$$

b. mass of Cd present = 112.4 g = 112.4 g

mass of S present = 32.07 g =   32.07 g

mass of O present = 4(16.00 g) = 64.00 g

molar mass of $CdSO_4$ = 208.5 g

$$\% \text{ Cd} = \frac{112.4 \text{ g Cd}}{208.5 \text{ g}} \times 100 = 53.91\% \text{ Cd}$$

$$\% \text{ S} = \frac{32.07 \text{ g S}}{208.5 \text{ g}} \times 100 = 15.38\% \text{ S}$$

$$\% \text{ O} = \frac{64.00 \text{ g O}}{208.5 \text{ g}} \times 100 = 30.70\% \text{ O}$$

c. mass of Fe present = 2(55.85 g) = 111.7 g

mass of S present = 3(32.07 g) = 96.21 g

mass of O present = 12(16.00 g) = 192.0 g

molar mass of $Fe_2(SO_4)_3$ = 399.9 g

$$\% \text{ Fe} = \frac{111.7 \text{ g Fe}}{399.9 \text{ g}} \times 100 = 27.93\% \text{ Fe}$$

$$\% \text{ S} = \frac{96.21 \text{ g S}}{399.9 \text{ g}} \times 100 = 24.06\% \text{ S}$$

$$\% \text{ O} = \frac{192.0 \text{ g O}}{399.9 \text{ g}} \times 100 = 48.01\% \text{ O}$$

d. mass of Mn present = 54.94 g = 54.94 g

mass of Cl present = 2(35.45 g) = 70.90 g

molar mass of $MnCl_2$ = 125.84 g

$$\% \text{ Mn} = \frac{54.94 \text{ g Mn}}{125.84 \text{ g}} \times 100 = 43.66\% \text{ Mn}$$

$$\% \text{ Cl} = \frac{70.90 \text{ g Cl}}{125.84 \text{ g}} \times 100 = 56.34\% \text{ Cl}$$

e.   mass of N present = 2(14.01 g) = 28.02 g

mass of H present = 8(1.008 g) = 8.064 g

mass of C present = 12.01 g = 12.01 g

mass of O present = 3(16.00 g) = 48.00 g

molar mass of $(NH_4)_2CO_3$ = 96.09 g

$$\% \, N = \frac{28.02 \text{ g N}}{96.09 \text{ g}} \times 100 = 29.16\% \text{ N}$$

$$\% \, H = \frac{8.064 \text{ g H}}{96.09 \text{ g}} \times 100 = 8.392\% \text{ H}$$

$$\% \, C = \frac{12.01 \text{ g C}}{96.09 \text{ g}} \times 100 = 12.50\% \text{ C}$$

$$\% \, O = \frac{48.00 \text{ g O}}{96.09 \text{ g}} \times 100 = 49.95\% \text{ O}$$

f.   mass of Na present =   22.99 g = 22.99 g

mass of H present = 1.008 g = 1.008 g

mass of C present = 12.01 g = 12.01 g

mass of O present = 3(16.00 g) = 48.00 g

molar mass of $NaHCO_3$ = 84.01 g

$$\% \, Na = \frac{22.99 \text{ g Na}}{84.01 \text{ g}} \times 100 = 27.37\% \text{ Na}$$

$$\% \, H = \frac{1.008 \text{ g H}}{84.01 \text{ g}} \times 100 = 1.200\% \text{ H}$$

$$\% \, C = \frac{12.01 \text{ g C}}{84.01 \text{ g}} \times 100 = 14.30\% \text{ C}$$

$$\% \, O = \frac{48.00 \text{ g O}}{84.01 \text{ g}} \times 100 = 57.14\% \text{ O}$$

g.   mass of C present = 12.01 g = 12.01 g

mass of O present = 2(16.00 g) = 32.00 g

molar mass of CO_2 =   44.01 g

$$\% \, C = \frac{12.01 \text{ g C}}{44.01 \text{ g}} \times 100 = 27.29\% \text{ C}$$

$$\% \, O = \frac{32.00 \text{ g O}}{44.01 \text{ g}} \times 100 = 72.71\% \text{ O}$$

h.   mass of Ag present = 107.9 g   = 107.9 g

mass of N present = 14.01 g = 14.01 g

mass of O present = 3(16.00 g) = 48.00 g

molar mass of $AgNO_3$ = 169.9 g

$$\% \text{ Ag} = \frac{107.9 \text{ g Ag}}{169.9 \text{ g}} \times 100 = 63.51\% \text{ Ag}$$

$$\% \text{ N} = \frac{14.01 \text{ g N}}{169.9 \text{ g}} \times 100 = 8.246\% \text{ N}$$

$$\% \text{ O} = \frac{48.00 \text{ g O}}{169.9 \text{ g}} \times 100 = 28.25\% \text{ O}$$

120.   a. $$\% \text{ Fe} = \frac{55.85 \text{ g Fe}}{151.92 \text{ g}} \times 100 = 36.76\% \text{ Fe}$$

b. $$\% \text{ Ag} = \frac{215.8 \text{ g Ag}}{231.8 \text{ g}} \times 100 = 93.10\% \text{ Ag}$$

c. $$\% \text{ Sr} = \frac{87.62 \text{ g Sr}}{158.5 \text{ g}} \times 100 = 55.28\% \text{ Sr}$$

d. $$\% \text{ C} = \frac{48.04 \text{ g C}}{86.09 \text{ g}} \times 100 = 55.80\% \text{ C}$$

e. $$\% \text{ C} = \frac{12.01 \text{ g C}}{32.04 \text{ g}} \times 100 = 37.48\% \text{ C}$$

f. $$\% \text{ Al} = \frac{53.96 \text{ g Al}}{101.96 \text{ g}} \times 100 = 52.92\% \text{ Al}$$

g. $$\% \text{ K} = \frac{39.10 \text{ g K}}{106.55 \text{ g}} \times 100 = 36.70\% \text{ K}$$

h. $$\% \text{ K} = \frac{39.10 \text{ g K}}{74.55 \text{ g}} \times 100 = 52.45\% \text{ K}$$

122. $$0.2990 \text{ g C} \times \frac{1 \text{ mol}}{12.01 \text{ g}} = 0.02490 \text{ mol C}$$

$$0.05849 \text{ g H} \times \frac{1 \text{ mol}}{1.008 \text{ g}} = 0.05803 \text{ mol H}$$

$$0.2318 \text{ g N} \times \frac{1 \text{ mol}}{14.01 \text{ g}} = 0.01655 \text{ mol N}$$

$$0.1328 \text{ g O} \times \frac{1 \text{ mol}}{16.00 \text{ g}} = 0.008300 \text{ mol O}$$

Dividing each number of moles by the smallest number of moles (0.008300 mol) gives

$$\frac{0.02490 \text{ mol C}}{0.008300} = 3.000 \text{ mol C} \qquad \frac{0.05803 \text{ mol H}}{0.008300} = 6.992 \text{ mol H}$$

$$\frac{0.01655 \text{ mol N}}{0.008300} = 1.994 \text{ mol N} \qquad \frac{0.008300 \text{ mol O}}{0.008300} = 1.000 \text{ mol O}$$

The empirical formula is $C_3H_7N_2O$.

124. Mass of oxygen in compound = 4.33 g – 4.01 g = 0.32 g O

$$4.01 \text{ g Hg} \times \frac{1 \text{ mol}}{200.6 \text{ g}} = 0.0200 \text{ mol Hg}$$

$$0.32 \text{ g O} \times \frac{1 \text{ mol}}{16.00 \text{ g}} = 0.020 \text{ mol O}$$

Since the numbers of moles are equal, the empirical formula is HgO.

126. Assume we have 100.0 g of the compound.

$$65.95 \text{ g Ba} \times \frac{1 \text{ mol}}{137.3 \text{ g}} = 0.4803 \text{ mol Ba}$$

$$34.05 \text{ g Cl} \times \frac{1 \text{ mol}}{35.45 \text{ g}} = 0.9605 \text{ mol Cl}$$

Dividing each of these number of moles by the smaller number gives

$$\frac{0.4803 \text{ mol Ba}}{0.4803 \text{ mol}} = 1.000 \text{ mol Ba} \qquad \frac{0.9605 \text{ mol Cl}}{0.4803 \text{ mol}} = 2.000 \text{ mol Cl}$$

The empirical formula is then $BaCl_2$.

CHAPTER 9

Chemical Quantities

2.   The coefficients of the balanced chemical equation for a reaction indicate the *relative numbers of moles* of each reactant that combine during the process, as well as the number of moles of each product formed.

4.   Balanced chemical equations tell us in what molar ratios substances combine to form products, not in what mass proportions they combine.

6.   a. $(NH_4)_2CO_3(s) \rightarrow 2NH_3(g) + CO_2(g) + H_2O(g)$

One formula unit of solid ammonium carbonate decomposes to produce two molecules of ammonia gas, one molecule of carbon dioxide gas, and one molecule of water vapor. One mole of solid ammonium carbonate decomposes into two moles of gaseous ammonia, one mole of carbon dioxide gas, and one mole of water vapor.

b. $6Mg(s) + P_4(s) \rightarrow 2Mg_3P_2(s)$

Six atoms of magnesium metal react with one molecule of solid phosphorus (P_4) to make two formula units of solid magnesium phosphide. Six moles of magnesium metal react with one mole of phosphorus solid (P_4) to produce two moles of solid magnesium phosphide.

c. $4Si(s) + S_8(s) \rightarrow 2Si_2S_4(l)$

Four atoms of solid silicon react with one molecule of solid sulfur (S_8) to form two molecules of liquid disilicon tetrasulfide. Four moles of solid silicon react with one mole of solid sulfur (S_8) to form two moles of liquid disilicon tetrasulfide.

d. $C_2H_5OH(l) + 3O_2(g) \rightarrow 2CO_2(g) + 3H_2O(g)$

One molecule of liquid ethanol burns with three molecules of oxygen gas to produce two molecules of carbon dioxide gas and three molecules of water vapor. One mole of liquid ethanol burns with three moles of oxygen gas to produce two moles of gaseous carbon dioxide and three moles of water vapor.

8.   Balanced chemical equations tell us in what molar ratios substances combine to form products, not in what mass proportions they combine. How could 2 grams of reactant produce a total of 3 grams of products?

10. $Fe_2O_3(s) + 3H_2SO_4(aq) \rightarrow Fe_2(SO_4)_3(s) + 3H_2O(l)$

For converting from a given number of moles of iron(III) oxide to the number of moles of sulfuric acid required, the mole ratio is

$$\left(\frac{3 \text{ mol } H_2SO_4}{1 \text{ mol } Fe_2O_3} \right)$$

For a given number of moles of iron(III) oxide reacting completely, the mole ratios used to calculate the number of moles of each product are

For $Fe_2(SO_4)_3$: $\left(\dfrac{1 \text{ mol } Fe_2(SO_4)_3}{1 \text{ mol } Fe_2O_3} \right)$ 　　　　For H_2O: $\left(\dfrac{3 \text{ mol } H_2O}{1 \text{ mol } Fe_2O_3} \right)$

12.　a.　$4Bi(s) + 3O_2(g) \rightarrow 2Bi_2O_3(s)$

$0.250 \text{ mol } Bi \times \dfrac{2 \text{ mol } Bi_2O_3}{4 \text{ mol } Bi} = 0.125 \text{ mol } Bi_2O_3$

　　b.　$SnO_2(s) + 2H_2(g) \rightarrow Sn(s) + 2H_2O(g)$

$0.250 \text{ mol } SnO_2 \times \dfrac{1 \text{ mol } Sn}{1 \text{ mol } SnO_2} = 0.250 \text{ mol } Sn$

$0.250 \text{ mol } SnO_2 \times \dfrac{2 \text{ mol } H_2O}{1 \text{ mol } SnO_2} = 0.500 \text{ mol } H_2O$

　　c.　$SiCl_4(l) + 2H_2O(l) \rightarrow SiO_2(s) + 4HCl(g)$

$0.250 \text{ mol } SiCl_4 \times \dfrac{1 \text{ mol } SiO_2}{1 \text{ mol } SiCl_4} = 0.250 \text{ mol } SiO_2$

$0.250 \text{ mol } SiCl_4 \times \dfrac{4 \text{ mol } HCl}{1 \text{ mol } SiCl_4} = 1.00 \text{ mol } HCl$

　　d.　$2N_2(g) + 5O_2(g) + 2H_2O(l) \rightarrow 4HNO_3(aq)$

$0.250 \text{ mol } N_2 \times \dfrac{4 \text{ mol } HNO_3}{2 \text{ mol } N_2} = 0.500 \text{ mol } HNO_3$

14.　a.　$C_5H_{12}(l) + 8O_2(g) \rightarrow 5CO_2(g) + 6H_2O(l)$

molar masses: CO_2, 44.01 g; H_2O, 18.02 g

$0.750 \text{ mol } C_5H_{12} \times \dfrac{5 \text{ mol } CO_2}{1 \text{ mol } C_5H_{12}} = 3.75 \text{ mol } CO_2$

$3.75 \text{ mol } CO_2 \times \dfrac{44.01 \text{ g } CO_2}{1 \text{ mol } CO_2} = 165 \text{ g } CO_2$

$0.750 \text{ mol } C_5H_{12} \times \dfrac{6 \text{ mol } H_2O}{1 \text{ mol } C_5H_{12}} = 4.50 \text{ mol } H_2O$

$4.50 \text{ mol } H_2O \times \dfrac{18.02 \text{ g } H_2O}{1 \text{ mol } H_2O} = 81.1 \text{ g } H_2O$

　　b.　$2CH_3OH(l) + 3O_2(g) \rightarrow 4H_2O(l) + 2CO_2(g)$

molar masses: H_2O, 18.02 g; CO_2, 44.01 g

$0.750 \text{ mol } CH_3OH \times \dfrac{4 \text{ mol } H_2O}{2 \text{ mol } CH_3OH} = 1.50 \text{ mol } H_2O$

$$1.50 \text{ mol } H_2O \times \frac{18.02 \text{ g } H_2O}{1 \text{ mol } H_2O} = 27.0 \text{ g } H_2O$$

$$0.750 \text{ mol } CH_3OH \times \frac{2 \text{ mol } CO_2}{2 \text{ mol } CH_3OH} = 0.750 \text{ mol } CO_2$$

$$0.750 \text{ mol } CO_2 \times \frac{44.01 \text{ g } CO_2}{1 \text{ mol } CO_2} = 33.0 \text{ g } CO_2$$

c. $Ba(OH)_2(aq) + H_3PO_4(aq) \rightarrow BaHPO_4(s) + 2H_2O(l)$

molar masses: $BaHPO_4$, 233.3 g; H_2O, 18.02 g

$$0.750 \text{ mol } Ba(OH)_2 \times \frac{1 \text{ mol } BaHPO_4}{1 \text{ mol } Ba(OH)_2} = 0.750 \text{ mol } BaHPO_4$$

$$0.750 \text{ mol } BaHPO_4 \times \frac{233.3 \text{ g } BaHPO_4}{1 \text{ mol } BaHPO_4} = 175 \text{ g } BaHPO_4$$

$$0.750 \text{ mol } Ba(OH)_2 \times \frac{2 \text{ mol } H_2O}{1 \text{ mol } Ba(OH)_2} = 1.50 \text{ mol } H_2O$$

$$1.50 \text{ mol } H_2O \times \frac{18.02 \text{ g } H_2O}{1 \text{ mol } H_2O} = 27.0 \text{ g } H_2O$$

d. $C_6H_{12}O_6(aq) \rightarrow 2C_2H_5OH(aq) + 2CO_2(g)$

molar masses: C_2H_5OH, 46.07 g; CO_2, 44.01 g

$$0.750 \text{ mol } C_6H_{12}O_6 \times \frac{2 \text{ mol } C_2H_5OH}{1 \text{ mol } C_6H_{12}O_6} = 1.50 \text{ mol } C_2H_5OH$$

$$1.50 \text{ mol } C_2H_5OH \times \frac{46.07 \text{ g } C_2H_5OH}{1 \text{ mol } C_2H_5OH} = 69.1 \text{ g } C_2H_5OH$$

$$0.750 \text{ mol } C_6H_{12}O_6 \times \frac{2 \text{ mol } CO_2}{1 \text{ mol } C_6H_{12}O_6} = 1.50 \text{ mol } CO_2$$

$$1.50 \text{ mol } CO_2 \times \frac{44.01 \text{ g } CO_2}{1 \text{ mol } CO_2} = 66.0 \text{ g } CO_2$$

16.   Before doing the calculations, the equations must be *balanced*.

a. $4KO_2(s) + 2H_2O(l) \rightarrow 3O_2(g) + 4KOH(s)$

$$0.625 \text{ mol } KOH \times \frac{3 \text{ mol } O_2}{4 \text{ mol } KOH} = 0.469 \text{ mol } O_2$$

b. $SeO_2(g) + 2H_2Se(g) \rightarrow 3Se(s) + 2H_2O(g)$

$$0.625 \text{ mol } H_2O \times \frac{3 \text{ mol } Se}{2 \text{ mol } H_2O} = 0.938 \text{ mol } Se$$

c. $2CH_3CH_2OH(l) + O_2(g) \rightarrow 2CH_3CHO(aq) + 2H_2O(l)$

$$0.625 \text{ mol } H_2O \times \frac{2 \text{ mol } CH_3CHO}{2 \text{ mol } H_2O} = 0.625 \text{ mol } CH_3CHO$$

d. $Fe_2O_3(s) + 2Al(s) \rightarrow 2Fe(l) + Al_2O_3(s)$

$$0.625 \text{ mol } Al_2O_3 \times \frac{2 \text{ mol } Fe}{1 \text{ mol } Al_2O_3} = 1.25 \text{ mol } Fe$$

18.   Stoichiometry is the process of using a chemical equation to calculate the relative masses of reactants and products involved in a reaction.

20.   a.   molar mass Ar = 39.95 g

$$72.4 \text{ mg Ar} \times \frac{1 \text{ g}}{1000 \text{ mg}} \times \frac{1 \text{ mol Ar}}{39.95 \text{ g Ar}} = 1.81 \times 10^{-3} \text{ mol Ar}$$

b.   molar mass CS_2 = 76.15 g

$$52.7 \text{ g } CS_2 \times \frac{1 \text{ mol } CS_2}{76.15 \text{ g } CS_2} = 0.692 \text{ mol } CS_2$$

c.   molar mass Fe = 55.85 g

$$784 \text{ kg Fe} \times \frac{1000 \text{ g}}{1 \text{ kg}} \times \frac{1 \text{ mol Fe}}{55.85 \text{ g Fe}} = 1.40 \times 10^4 \text{ mol Fe}$$

d.   molar mass $CaCl_2$ = 110.98 g

$$0.00104 \text{ g } CaCl_2 \times \frac{1 \text{ mol } CaCl_2}{110.98 \text{ g } CaCl_2} = 9.37 \times 10^{-6} \text{ mol } CaCl_2$$

e.   molar mass NiS = 90.76 g

$$1.26 \times 10^3 \text{ g NiS} \times \frac{1 \text{ mol NiS}}{90.76 \text{ g NiS}} = 13.9 \text{ mol NiS}$$

22.   a.   molar mass of C_3H_8 = 44.09 g

$$2.23 \text{ mol } C_3H_8 \times \frac{44.09 \text{ g } C_3H_8}{1 \text{ mol } C_3H_8} = 98.3 \text{ g } C_3H_8$$

b.   molar mass of Ar = 39.95 g; 9.03 millimol = 0.00903 mol

$$0.00903 \text{ mol Ar} \times \frac{39.95 \text{ g Ar}}{1 \text{ mol Ar}} = 0.361 \text{ g Ar}$$

c.   molar mass of SiO_2 = 60.09 g

$$5.91 \times 10^6 \text{ mol } SiO_2 \times \frac{60.09 \text{ g } SiO_2}{1 \text{ mol } SiO_2} = 3.55 \times 10^8 \text{ g } SiO_2$$

d.   molar mass of $CuCl_2$ = 134.45 g

$$0.000104 \text{ mol } CuCl_2 \times \frac{134.45 \text{ g } CuCl_2}{1 \text{ mol } CuCl_2} = 0.0140 \text{ g } CuCl_2$$

e.   molar mass of CuCl = 99.00 g

$$0.000104 \text{ mol } CuCl \times \frac{99.00 \text{ g } CuCl}{1 \text{ mol } CuCl} = 0.0103 \text{ g } CuCl$$

24.   Before any calculations are done, the equations must be *balanced*.

a. $2Al(s) + 3Br_2(l) \rightarrow 2AlBr_3(s)$

molar mass Al = 26.98 g

$$0.557 \text{ g Al} \times \frac{1 \text{ mol Al}}{26.98 \text{ g Al}} \times \frac{3 \text{ mol } Br_2}{2 \text{ mol Al}} = 0.0310 \text{ mol } Br_2$$

b. $Hg(s) + 2HClO_4(aq) \rightarrow Hg(ClO_4)_2(aq) + H_2(g)$

molar mass Hg = 200.6 g

$$0.557 \text{ g Hg} \times \frac{1 \text{ mol Hg}}{200.6 \text{ g}} \times \frac{2 \text{ mol } HClO_4}{1 \text{ mol Hg}} = 0.00555 \text{ mol } HClO_4$$

c. $3K(s) + P(s) \rightarrow K_3P(s)$

molar mass K = 39.10 g

$$0.557 \text{ g K} \times \frac{1 \text{ mol K}}{39.10 \text{ g K}} \times \frac{1 \text{ mol P}}{3 \text{ mol K}} = 0.00475 \text{ mol P}$$

d. $CH_4(g) + 4Cl_2(g) \rightarrow CCl_4(l) + 4HCl(g)$

molar mass CH_4 = 16.04 g

$$0.557 \text{ g } CH_4 \times \frac{1 \text{ mol } CH_4}{16.04 \text{ g } CH_4} \times \frac{4 \text{ mol } Cl_2}{1 \text{ mol } CH_4} = 0.139 \text{ mol } Cl_2$$

26.   a. $2BCl_3(s) + 3H_2(g) \rightarrow 2B(s) + 6HCl(g)$

molar masses: BCl_3, 117.16 g; B, 10.81 g; HCl, 36.46 g

$$15.0 \text{ g } BCl_3 \times \frac{1 \text{ mol } BCl_3}{117.16 \text{ g } BCl_3} = 0.128 \text{ mol } BCl_3$$

$$0.128 \text{ mol } BCl_3 \times \frac{2 \text{ mol B}}{2 \text{ mol } BCl_3} \times \frac{10.81 \text{ g B}}{1 \text{ mol B}} = 1.38 \text{ g B}$$

$$0.128 \text{ mol } BCl_3 \times \frac{6 \text{ mol HCl}}{2 \text{ mol } BCl_3} \times \frac{36.46 \text{ g HCl}}{1 \text{ mol HCl}} = 14.0 \text{ g HCl}$$

b. $2Cu_2S(s) + 3O_2(g) \rightarrow 2Cu_2O(s) + 2SO_2(g)$

molar masses: Cu_2S, 159.17 g; Cu_2O, 143.1 g; SO_2, 64.07 g

$$15.0 \text{ g Cu}_2\text{S} \times \frac{1 \text{ mol Cu}_2\text{S}}{159.17 \text{ g Cu}_2\text{S}} = 0.09424 \text{ mol Cu}_2\text{S}$$

$$0.09424 \text{ mol Cu}_2\text{S} \times \frac{2 \text{ mol Cu}_2\text{O}}{2 \text{ mol Cu}_2\text{S}} \times \frac{143.1 \text{ g Cu}_2\text{O}}{1 \text{ mol Cu}_2\text{O}} = 13.5 \text{ g Cu}_2\text{O}$$

$$0.09424 \text{ mol Cu}_2\text{S} \times \frac{2 \text{ mol SO}_2}{2 \text{ mol Cu}_2\text{S}} \times \frac{64.07 \text{ g SO}_2}{1 \text{ mol SO}_2} = 6.04 \text{ g SO}_2$$

c. $2\text{Cu}_2\text{O}(s) + \text{Cu}_2\text{S}(s) \rightarrow 6\text{Cu}(s) + \text{SO}_2(g)$

molar masses: Cu_2S, 159.17 g; Cu, 63.55 g; SO_2, 64.07 g

$$15.0 \text{ g Cu}_2\text{S} \times \frac{1 \text{ mol Cu}_2\text{S}}{159.17 \text{ g Cu}_2\text{S}} = 0.09424 \text{ mol Cu}_2\text{S}$$

$$0.09424 \text{ mol Cu}_2\text{S} \times \frac{6 \text{ mol Cu}}{1 \text{ mol Cu}_2\text{S}} \times \frac{63.55 \text{ g Cu}}{1 \text{ mol Cu}} = 35.9 \text{ g Cu}$$

$$0.09424 \text{ mol Cu}_2\text{S} \times \frac{1 \text{ mol SO}_2}{1 \text{ mol Cu}_2\text{S}} \times \frac{64.07 \text{ g SO}_2}{1 \text{ mol SO}_2} = 6.04 \text{ g SO}_2$$

d. $\text{CaCO}_3(s) + \text{SiO}_2(s) \rightarrow \text{CaSiO}_3(s) + \text{CO}_2(g)$

molar masses: SiO_2, 60.09 g; CaSiO_3, 116.17 g; CO_2, 44.01 g

$$15.0 \text{ g SiO}_2 \times \frac{1 \text{ mol SiO}_2}{60.09 \text{ g SiO}_2} = 0.2496 \text{ mol SiO}_2$$

$$0.2496 \text{ mol SiO}_2 \times \frac{1 \text{ mol CaSiO}_3}{1 \text{ mol SiO}_2} \times \frac{116.17 \text{ g CaSiO}_3}{1 \text{ mol CaSiO}_3} = 29.0 \text{ g CaSiO}_3$$

$$0.2496 \text{ mol SiO}_2 \times \frac{1 \text{ mol CO}_2}{1 \text{ mol SiO}_2} \times \frac{44.01 \text{ g CO}_2}{1 \text{ mol CO}_2} = 11.0 \text{ g CO}_2$$

28.   The balanced equation for the reaction is:

$\text{CaC}_2(s) + 2\text{H}_2\text{O}(l) \rightarrow \text{C}_2\text{H}_2(g) + \text{Ca(OH)}_2(s)$

molar masses: CaC_2, 64.10 g; C_2H_2, 26.04 g

$$3.75 \text{ g CaC}_2 \times \frac{1 \text{ mol CaC}_2}{64.10 \text{ g CaC}_2} = 0.0585 \text{ mol CaC}_2$$

$$0.0585 \text{ mol CaC}_2 \times \frac{1 \text{ mol C}_2\text{H}_2}{1 \text{ mol CaC}_2} = 0.0585 \text{ mol C}_2\text{H}_2$$

$$0.0585 \text{ mol C}_2\text{H}_2 \times \frac{26.04 \text{ g C}_2\text{H}_2}{1 \text{ mol C}_2\text{H}_2} = 1.52 \text{ g C}_2\text{H}_2$$

30. $2\text{NaHCO}_3(s) \rightarrow \text{Na}_2\text{CO}_3(s) + \text{H}_2\text{O}(g) + \text{CO}_2(g)$

molar masses: NaHCO_3, 84.01 g; Na_2CO_3, 106.0 g

$$1.52 \text{ g NaHCO}_3 \times \frac{1 \text{ mol NaHCO}_3}{84.01 \text{ g NaHCO}_3} = 0.01809 \text{ mol NaHCO}_3$$

$$0.01809 \text{ mol NaHCO}_3 \times \frac{1 \text{ mol Na}_2\text{CO}_3}{2 \text{ mol NaHCO}_3} = 0.009047 \text{ mol Na}_2\text{CO}_3$$

$$0.009047 \text{ mol Na}_2\text{CO}_3 \times \frac{106.0 \text{ g Na}_2\text{CO}_3}{1 \text{ mol Na}_2\text{CO}_3} = 0.959 \text{ g Na}_2\text{CO}_3$$

32. $C_6H_{12}O_6(aq) \rightarrow 2C_2H_5OH(aq) + 2CO_2(g)$

molar masses: $C_6H_{12}O_6$, 180.2 g; C_2H_5OH, 46.07 g

$$5.25 \text{ g C}_6\text{H}_{12}\text{O}_6 \times \frac{1 \text{ mol C}_6\text{H}_{12}\text{O}_6}{180.2 \text{ g C}_6\text{H}_{12}\text{O}_6} = 0.02913 \text{ mol C}_6\text{H}_{12}\text{O}_6$$

$$0.02913 \text{ mol C}_6\text{H}_{12}\text{O}_6 \times \frac{2 \text{ mol C}_2\text{H}_5\text{OH}}{1 \text{ mol C}_6\text{H}_{12}\text{O}_6} = 0.5826 \text{ mol C}_2\text{H}_5\text{OH}$$

$$0.5286 \text{ mol C}_2\text{H}_5\text{OH} \times \frac{46.07 \text{ g C}_2\text{H}_5\text{OH}}{1 \text{ mol C}_2\text{H}_5\text{OH}} = 2.68 \text{ g ethyl alcohol}$$

34. $NH_4Cl(s) + NaOH(s) \rightarrow NH_3(g) + NaCl(s) + H_2O(g)$

molar masses: NH_4Cl, 53.49 g; NH_3, 17.03 g

$$1.39 \text{ g NH}_4\text{Cl} \times \frac{1 \text{ mol NH}_4\text{Cl}}{53.49 \text{ g NH}_4\text{Cl}} = 0.02599 \text{ mol NH}_4\text{Cl}$$

$$0.02599 \text{ mol NH}_4\text{Cl} \times \frac{1 \text{ mol NH}_3}{1 \text{ mol NH}_4\text{Cl}} = 0.02599 \text{ mol NH}_3$$

$$0.02599 \text{ mol NH}_3 \times \frac{17.03 \text{ g NH}_3}{1 \text{ mol NH}_3} = 0.443 \text{ g NH}_3$$

36. $4HgS(s) + 4CaO(s) \rightarrow 4Hg(l) + 3CaS(s) + CaSO_4(s)$

molar masses: HgS, 232.7 g Hg, 200.6 g; 10.0 kg = 1.00×10^4 g

$$1.00 \times 10^4 \text{ g HgS} \times \frac{1 \text{ mol HgS}}{232.7 \text{ g HgS}} = 42.97 \text{ mol HgS}$$

$$42.97 \text{ mol HgS} \times \frac{4 \text{ mol Hg}}{4 \text{ mol HgS}} = 42.97 \text{ mol Hg}$$

$$42.97 \text{ mol Hg} \times \frac{200.6 \text{ g Hg}}{1 \text{ mol Hg}} = 8.62 \times 10^3 \text{ g Hg} = 8.62 \text{ kg Hg}$$

38. $C_{12}H_{22}O_{11}(s) \rightarrow 12C(s) + 11H_2O(g)$

molar masses: $C_{12}H_{22}O_{11}$, 342.3 g; C, 12.01

$$1.19 \text{ g C}_{12}\text{H}_{22}\text{O}_{11} \times \frac{1 \text{ mol C}_{12}\text{H}_{22}\text{O}_{11}}{342.3 \text{ g C}_{12}\text{H}_{22}\text{O}_{11}} = 3.476 \times 10^{-3} \text{ mol C}_{12}\text{H}_{22}\text{O}_{11}$$

$$3.476 \times 10^{-3} \text{ mol C}_{12}\text{H}_{22}\text{O}_{11} \times \frac{12 \text{ mol C}}{1 \text{ mol C}_{12}\text{H}_{22}\text{O}_{11}} = 0.04172 \text{ mol C}$$

$$0.04172 \text{ mol C} \times \frac{12.01 \text{ g C}}{1 \text{ mol C}} = 0.501 \text{ g C}$$

40. The balanced equation is:

$$2C_8H_{18} + 25O_2 \rightarrow 16CO_2 + 18H_2O$$

molar masses: C_8H_{18}, 114.22 g; CO_2, 44.01 g   1 lb of CO_2 = 453.59 g CO_2

$$453.59 \text{ g CO}_2 \times \frac{1 \text{ mol CO}_2}{44.01 \text{ g CO}_2} = 10.31 \text{ mol CO}_2$$

From the balanced chemical equation, we can calculate the number of moles and number of grams of pure octane that would be required to produce 10.31 mol CO_2.

$$10.31 \text{ mol CO}_2 \times \frac{2 \text{ mol C}_8\text{H}_{18}}{16 \text{ mol CO}_2} = 1.288 \text{ mol C}_8\text{H}_{18}$$

$$1.288 \text{ mol C}_8\text{H}_{18} \times \frac{114.22 \text{ g C}_8\text{H}_{18}}{1 \text{ mol C}_8\text{H}_{18}} = 147.2 \text{ g C}_8\text{H}_{18}$$

From the density of C_8H_{18} we can calculate the volume of 147.2 g C_8H_{18}.

$$147.2 \text{ g C}_8\text{H}_{18} \times \frac{1 \text{ mL C}_8\text{H}_{18}}{0.75 \text{ g C}_8\text{H}_{18}} = 196.3 \text{ mL C}_8\text{H}_{18} \ (2.0 \times 10^2 \text{ mL to two significant figures})$$

From the preceding, we know that to travel 1 mile, we need approximately 200 mL of octane

$$\frac{1 \text{ mi}}{196.3 \text{ mL}} \times \frac{1000 \text{ mL}}{1 \text{ L}} \times \frac{3.7854 \text{ L}}{1 \text{ gal}} = \text{approximately 19 mi/gal}$$

42. To determine the limiting reactant, first calculate the number of moles of each reactant present. Then determine how these numbers of moles correspond to the stoichiometric ratio indicated by the balanced chemical equation for the reaction.

44. A reactant is present *in excess* if there is more of that reactant present than is needed to combine with the limiting reactant for the process. By definition, the limiting reactant cannot be present in excess. An excess of any reactant does not affect the theoretical yield for a process: the theoretical yield is determined by the limiting reactant.

46. a. $S(s) + 2H_2SO_4(aq) \rightarrow 3SO_2(g) + 2H_2O(l)$

Molar masses: S, 32.07 g; H_2SO_4, 98.09 g; SO_2, 64.07 g; H_2O, 18.02 g

$$5.00 \text{ g S} \times \frac{1 \text{ mol}}{32.07 \text{ g}} = 0.1559 \text{ mol S}$$

$$5.00 \text{ g } H_2SO_4 \times \frac{1 \text{ mol}}{98.09 \text{ g}} = 0.05097 \text{ mol } H_2SO_4$$

According to the balanced chemical equation, we would need twice as much sulfuric acid as sulfur for complete reaction of both reactants. We clearly have much less sulfuric acid present than sulfur: sulfuric acid is the limiting reactant. The calculation of the masses of products produced is based on the number of moles of the sulfuric acid.

$$0.05097 \text{ mol } H_2SO_4 \times \frac{3 \text{ mol } SO_2}{2 \text{ mol } H_2SO_4} \times \frac{64.07 \text{ g } SO_2}{1 \text{ mol } SO_2} = 4.90 \text{ g } SO_2$$

$$0.05097 \text{ mol } H_2SO_4 \times \frac{2 \text{ mol } H_2O}{2 \text{ mol } H_2SO_4} \times \frac{18.02 \text{ g } H_2O}{1 \text{ mol } H_2O} = 0.918 \text{ g } H_2O$$

b. $MnO_2(s) + 2H_2SO_4(aq) \rightarrow Mn(SO_4)_2 + 2H_2O(l)$

molar masses: MnO_2, 86.94 g; H_2SO_4 98.09 g; $Mn(SO_4)_2$, 247.1 g; H_2O, 18.02 g

$$5.00 \text{ g } MnO_2 \times \frac{1 \text{ mol}}{86.94 \text{ g}} = 0.05751 \text{ mol } MnO_2$$

$$5.00 \text{ g } H_2SO_4 \times \frac{1 \text{ mol}}{98.09 \text{ g}} = 0.05097 \text{ mol } H_2SO_4$$

According to the balanced chemical equation, we would need twice as much sulfuric acid as manganese(IV) oxide for complete reaction of both reactants. We do not have this much sulfuric acid, so sulfuric acid must be the limiting reactant. The amount of each product produced will be based on the sulfuric acid reacting completely.

$$0.05097 \text{ mol } H_2SO_4 \times \frac{1 \text{ mol } Mn(SO_4)_2}{2 \text{ mol } H2SO4} \times \frac{247.1 \text{ g } Mn(SO_4)_2}{1 \text{ mol } Mn(SO_4)_2} = 6.30 \text{ g } Mn(SO_4)_2$$

$$0.05097 \text{ mol } H_2SO_4 \times \frac{2 \text{ mol } H_2O}{2 \text{ mol } H_2SO_4} \times \frac{18.02 \text{ g } H_2O}{1 \text{ mol } H_2O} = 0.918 \text{ g } H_2O$$

c. $2H_2S(g) + 3O_2(g) \rightarrow 2SO_2(g) + 2H_2O(l)$

Molar masses: H_2S, 34.09 g; O_2, 32.00 g; SO_2, 64.07 g; H_2O, 18.02 g

$$5.00 \text{ g } H_2S \times \frac{1 \text{ mol}}{34.09 \text{ g}} = 0.1467 \text{ mol } H_2S$$

$$5.00 \text{ g } O_2 \times \frac{1 \text{ mol}}{32.00 \text{ g}} = 0.1563 \text{ mol } O_2$$

According to the balanced equation, we would need 1.5 times as much O_2 as H_2S for complete reaction of both reactants. We don't have that much O_2, so O_2 must be the limiting reactant that will control the masses of each product produced.

$$0.1563 \text{ mol } O_2 \times \frac{2 \text{ mol } SO_2}{3 \text{ mol } O_2} \times \frac{64.07 \text{ g } SO_2}{1 \text{ mol } SO_2} = 6.67 \text{ g } SO_2$$

$$0.1563 \text{ mol } O_2 \times \frac{2 \text{ mol } H_2O}{3 \text{ mol } O_2} \times \frac{18.02 \text{ g } H_2O}{1 \text{ mol } H_2O} = 1.88 \text{ g } H_2O$$

d. $3AgNO_3(aq) + Al(s) \rightarrow 3Ag(s) + Al(NO_3)_3(aq)$

Molar masses: $AgNO_3$, 169.9 g; Al, 26.98 g; Ag, 107.9 g; $Al(NO_3)_3$, 213.0 g

$$5.00 \text{ g AgNO}_3 \times \frac{1 \text{ mol}}{169.9 \text{ g}} = 0.02943 \text{ mol AgNO}_3$$

$$5.00 \text{ g Al} \times \frac{1 \text{ mol}}{26.98 \text{ g}} = 0.1853 \text{ mol Al}$$

According to the balanced chemical equation, we would need three moles of $AgNO_3$ for every mole of Al for complete reaction of both reactants. We in fact have fewer moles of $AgNO_3$ than aluminum, so $AgNO_3$ must be the limiting reactant. The amount of product produced is calculated from the number of moles of the limiting reactant present:

$$0.02943 \text{ mol AgNO}_3 \times \frac{3 \text{ mol Ag}}{3 \text{ mol AgNO}_3} \times \frac{107.9 \text{ g Ag}}{1 \text{ mol Ag}} = 3.18 \text{ g Ag}$$

$$0.02943 \text{ mol AgNO}_3 \times \frac{1 \text{ mol Al(NO}_3)_3}{3 \text{ mol AgNO}_3} \times \frac{213.0 \text{ g Al(NO}_3)_3}{1 \text{ mol Al(NO}_3)_3} = 2.09 \text{ g}$$

48. a. $CS_2(l) + 3O_2(g) \rightarrow CO_2(g) + 2SO_2(g)$

Molar masses: CS_2, 76.15 g; O_2, 32.00 g; CO_2, 44.01 g

$$1.00 \text{ g CS}_2 \times \frac{1 \text{ mol}}{76.15 \text{ g}} = 0.01313 \text{ mol CS}_2$$

$$1.00 \text{ g O}_2 \times \frac{1 \text{ mol}}{32.00 \text{ g}} = 0.03125 \text{ mol O}_2$$

From the balanced chemical equation, we would need three times as much oxygen as carbon disulfide for complete reaction of both reactants. We do not have this much oxygen, and so oxygen must be the limiting reactant.

$$0.03125 \text{ mol O}_2 \times \frac{1 \text{ mol CO}_2}{3 \text{ mol O}_2} \times \frac{44.01 \text{ g CO}_2}{1 \text{ mol CO}_2} = 0.458 \text{ g CO}_2$$

b. $2NH_3(g) + CO_2(g) \rightarrow CN_2H_4O(s) + H_2O(l)$

Molar masses: NH_3, 17.03 g; CO_2, 44.01 g; H_2O, 18.02 g

$$1.00 \text{ g NH}_3 \times \frac{1 \text{ mol}}{17.03 \text{ g}} = 0.05872 \text{ mol NH}_3$$

$$1.00 \text{ g CO}_2 \times \frac{1 \text{ mol}}{44.01 \text{ g}} = 0.02272 \text{ mol CO}_2$$

The balanced chemical equation tells us that we would need twice as many moles of ammonia as carbon dioxide for complete reaction of both reactants. We have *more* than this amount of ammonia present, so the reaction will be limited by the amount of carbon dioxide present.

$$0.02272 \text{ mol CO}_2 \times \frac{1 \text{ mol H}_2\text{O}}{1 \text{ mol CO}_2} \times \frac{18.02 \text{ g H}_2\text{O}}{1 \text{ mol H}_2\text{O}} = 0.409 \text{ g H}_2\text{O}$$

c. $H_2(g) + MnO_2(s) \rightarrow MnO(s) + H_2O(l)$

Molar masses: H_2, 2.016 g; MnO_2, 86.94 g; H_2O, 18.02 g

$$1.00 \text{ g H}_2 \times \frac{1 \text{ mol}}{2.016 \text{ g}} = 0.496 \text{ mol H}_2$$

$$1.00 \text{ g MnO}_2 \times \frac{1 \text{ mol}}{86.94 \text{ g}} = 0.0115 \text{ mol MnO}_2$$

Because the coefficients of both reactants in the balanced chemical equation are the same, we would need equal amounts of both reactants for complete reaction. Therefore, manganese(IV) oxide must be the limiting reactant and controls the amount of product obtained.

$$0.0115 \text{ mol MnO}_2 \times \frac{1 \text{ mol H}_2\text{O}}{1 \text{ mol MnO}_2} \times \frac{18.02 \text{ g H}_2\text{O}}{1 \text{ mol H}_2\text{O}} = 0.207 \text{ g H}_2\text{O}$$

d. $I_2(s) + Cl_2(g) \rightarrow 2ICl(g)$

Molar masses: I_2, 253.8 g; Cl_2, 70.90 g; ICl, 162.35 g

$$1.00 \text{ g I}_2 \times \frac{1 \text{ mol}}{253.8 \text{ g}} = 0.00394 \text{ mol I}_2$$

$$1.00 \text{ g Cl}_2 \times \frac{1 \text{ mol}}{70.90 \text{ g}} = 0.0141 \text{ mol Cl}_2$$

From the balanced chemical equation, we would need equal amounts of I_2 and Cl_2 for complete reaction of both reactants. As we have much less iodine than chlorine, iodine must be the limiting reactant.

$$0.00394 \text{ mol I}_2 \times \frac{2 \text{ mol ICl}}{1 \text{ mol I}_2} \times \frac{162.35 \text{ g ICl}}{1 \text{ mol ICl}} = 1.28 \text{ g ICl}$$

50.   a. $CO(g) + 2H_2(g) \rightarrow CH_3OH(l)$

CO is the limiting reactant; 11.4 mg CH_3OH

      b. $2Al(s) + 3I_2(s) \rightarrow 2AlI_3(s)$

I_2 is the limiting reactant; 10.7 mg AlI_3

      c. $Ca(OH)_2(aq) + 2HBr(aq) \rightarrow CaBr_2(aq) + 2H_2O(l)$

HBr is the limiting reactant; 12.4 mg $CaBr_2$; 2.23 mg H_2O

      d. $2Cr(s) + 2H_3PO_4(aq) \rightarrow 2CrPO_4(s) + 3H_2(g)$

H_3PO_4 is the limiting reactant; 15.0 mg $CrPO_4$; 0.309 mg H_2

52. $CuO(s) + H_2SO_4(aq) \rightarrow CuSO_4(aq) + H_2O(l)$

molar masses: CuO, 79.55 g; H_2SO_4, 98.09 g

$$2.49 \text{ g CuO} \times \frac{1 \text{ mol CuO}}{79.55 \text{ g CuO}} = 0.0313 \text{ mol CuO}$$

$$5.05 \text{ g H}_2\text{SO}_4 \times \frac{1 \text{ mol H}_2\text{SO}_4}{98.09 \text{ g H}_2\text{SO}_4} = 0.0515 \text{ mol H}_2\text{SO}_4$$

Since the reaction is of 1:1 stoichiometry, CuO must be the limiting reactant since it is present in the lesser amount on a molar basis.

54. $4\text{Fe}(s) + 3\text{O}_2(g) \rightarrow 2\text{Fe}_2\text{O}_3(s)$

Molar masses: Fe, 55.85 g; Fe$_2$O$_3$, 159.7 g

$$1.25 \text{ g Fe} \times \frac{1 \text{ mol}}{55.85 \text{ g}} = 0.0224 \text{ mol Fe present}$$

Calculate how many mol of O$_2$ are required to react with this amount of Fe

$$0.0224 \text{ mol Fe} \times \frac{3 \text{ mol O}_2}{4 \text{ mol Fe}} = 0.0168 \text{ mol O}_2$$

Because we have more O$_2$ than this, Fe must be the limiting reactant.

$$0.0224 \text{ mol Fe} \times \frac{2 \text{ mol Fe}_2\text{O}_3}{4 \text{ mol Fe}} \times \frac{159.7 \text{ g Fe}_2\text{O}_3}{1 \text{ mol Fe}_2\text{O}_3} = 1.79 \text{ g Fe}_2\text{O}_3$$

56. $\text{CaCl}_2(aq) + \text{Na}_2\text{SO}_4(aq) \rightarrow \text{CaSO}_4(s) + 2\text{NaCl}(aq)$

molar masses: CaCl$_2$, 110.98 g; Na$_2$SO$_4$, 142.05 g

$$5.21 \text{ g CaCl}_2 \times \frac{1 \text{ mol CaCl}_2}{110.98 \text{ g CaCl}_2} = 0.0469 \text{ mol CaCl}_2 = 0.0469 \text{ mol Ca}^{2+} \text{ ion}$$

$$4.95 \text{ g Na}_2\text{SO}_4 \times \frac{1 \text{ mol Na}_2\text{SO}_4}{142.05 \text{ g Na}_2\text{SO}_4} = 0.0348 \text{ mol Na}_2\text{SO}_4 = 0.0348 \text{ mol SO}_4^{2-} \text{ ion}$$

Because the balanced chemical equation indicates a 1:1 stoichiometry for the reaction, there is not nearly enough sulfate ion present (0.0348 mol) to precipitate the amount of calcium ion in the sample (0.0469 mol). Sodium sulfate (sulfate ion) is the limiting reactant. Calcium chloride (calcium ion) is present in excess.

58. $\text{SiO}_2(s) + 3\text{C}(s) \rightarrow 2\text{CO}(g) + \text{SiC}(s)$

molar masses: SiO$_2$, 60.09 g; SiC, 40.10 g; 1.0 kg = 1.0×10^3 g

$$1.0 \times 10^3 \text{ g SiO}_2 \times \frac{1 \text{ mol}}{60.09 \text{ g}} = 16.64 \text{ mol SiO}_2$$

From the balanced chemical equation, if 16.64 mol of SiO$_2$ were to react completely (an excess of carbon is present), then 16.64 mol of SiC should be produced (the coefficients of SiO$_2$ and SiC are the same).

$$16.64 \text{ mol SiC} \times \frac{40.01 \text{ g}}{1 \text{ mol}} = 6.7 \times 10^2 \text{ g SiC} = 0.67 \text{ kg SiC}$$

60. If the reaction is performed in a solvent, the product may have a substantial solubility in the solvent; the reaction may come to equilibrium before the full yield of product is achieved (see Chapter 16); loss of product may occur through operator error.

62. $2KClO_3(s) \rightarrow 2KCl(s) + 3O_2(g)$

    molar mass: $KClO_3$, 122.55 g; O_2, 32.00 g

    $$4.74 \text{ g } KClO_3 \times \frac{1 \text{ mol } KClO_3}{122.55 \text{ g } KClO_3} = 0.0387 \text{ mol } KClO_3$$

    $$0.0387 \text{ mol } KClO_3 \times \frac{3 \text{ mol } O_2}{2 \text{ mol } KClO_3} = 0.0580 \text{ mol } O_2$$

    $$0.0580 \text{ mol } O_2 \times \frac{32.00 \text{ g } O_2}{1 \text{ mol } O_2} = 1.86 \text{ g } O_2 \text{ theoretical yield}$$

    $$\% \text{ yield} = \frac{1.51 \text{ g actual}}{1.86 \text{ g theoretical}} \times 100 = 81.3\% \text{ of theory}$$

64. $2LiOH(s) + CO_2(g) \rightarrow Li_2CO_3(s) + H_2O(g)$

    molar masses: LiOH, 23.95 g; CO_2, 44.01 g

    $$155 \text{ g LiOH} \times \frac{1 \text{ mol LiOH}}{23.95 \text{ g LiOH}} \times \frac{1 \text{ mol } CO_2}{2 \text{ mol LiOH}} \times \frac{44.01 \text{ g } CO_2}{1 \text{ mol } CO_2} = 142 \text{ g } CO_2$$

    As the cartridge has only absorbed 102 g CO_2 out of a total capacity of 142 g CO_2, the cartridge has absorbed

    $$\frac{102 \text{ g}}{142 \text{ g}} \times 100 = 71.8\% \text{ of its capacity.}$$

66. $Ba^{2+}(aq) + SO_4^{2-}(aq) \rightarrow BaSO_4(s)$

    molar masses: SO_4^{2-}, 96.07 g; $BaCl_2$, 208.2 g; $BaSO_4$, 233.4 g

    $$1.12 \text{ g } SO_4^{2-} \times \frac{1 \text{ mol}}{96.07 \text{ g}} = 0.01166 \text{ mol } SO_4^{2-}$$

    $$5.02 \text{ g } BaCl_2 \times \frac{1 \text{ mol}}{208.2 \text{ g}} = 0.02411 \text{ mol } BaCl_2 = 0.02411 \text{ mol } Ba^{2+}$$

    SO_4^{2-} is the limiting reactant.

    $$0.01166 \text{ mol } SO_4^{2-} \times \frac{1 \text{ mol } BaSO_4}{1 \text{ mol } SO_4^{2-}} \times \frac{233.4 \text{ g } BaSO_4}{1 \text{ mol } BaSO_4} = 2.72 \text{ g } BaSO_4$$

    $$\text{Percent yield} = \frac{\text{actual yield}}{\text{theoretical yield}} \times 100 = \frac{2.02 \text{ g}}{2.72 \text{ g}} \times 100 = 74.3\%$$

68. $NaCl(aq) + NH_3(aq) + H_2O(l) + CO_2(s) \rightarrow NH_4Cl(aq) + NaHCO_3(s)$

    molar masses: NH_3, 17.03 g; CO_2, 44.01 g; $NaHCO_3$, 84.01 g

$$10.0 \text{ g NH}_3 \times \frac{1 \text{ mol}}{17.03 \text{ g}} = 0.5872 \text{ mol NH}_3$$

$$15.0 \text{ g CO}_2 \times \frac{1 \text{ mol}}{44.01 \text{ g}} = 0.3408 \text{ mol CO}_2$$

CO_2 is the limiting reactant.

$$0.3408 \text{ mol CO}_2 \times \frac{1 \text{ mol NaHCO}_3}{1 \text{ mol CO}_2} = 0.3408 \text{ mol NaHCO}_3$$

$$0.3408 \text{ mol NaHCO}_3 \times \frac{84.01 \text{ g}}{1 \text{ mol}} = 28.6 \text{ g NaHCO}_3$$

70. $C_6H_{12}O_6(s) + 6O_2(g) \rightarrow 6CO_2(g) + 6H_2O(g)$

    molar masses: glucose, 180.2 g; CO_2, 44.01 g

    $$1.00 \text{ g glucose} \times = 5.549 \times 10^{-3} \text{ mol glucose}$$

    $$5.549 \times 10^{-3} \text{ mol glucose} \times \frac{6 \text{ mol CO}_2}{1 \text{ mol glucose}} = 3.33 \times 10^{-2} \text{ mol CO}_2$$

    $$3.33 \times 10^{-2} \text{ mol CO}_2 \times \frac{44.01 \text{ g}}{1 \text{ mol}} = 1.47 \text{ g CO}_2$$

72. $Ba^{2+}(aq) + SO_4^{2-}(aq) \rightarrow BaSO_4(s)$

    millimolar ionic masses: Ba^{2+}, 137.3 mg; SO_4^{2-}, 96.07 mg; $BaCl_2$, 208.2 mg

    $$150 \text{ mg SO}_4^{2-} \times \frac{1 \text{ mmol}}{96.07 \text{ mg}} = 1.56 \text{ millimol SO}_4^{2-}$$

    As barium ion and sulfate ion react on a 1:1 stoichiometric basis, then 1.56 millimol of barium ion is needed, which corresponds to 1.56 millimol of $BaCl_2$

    $$1.56 \text{ millimol BaCl}_2 \times \frac{208.2 \text{ mg}}{1 \text{ mmol}} = 325 \text{ milligrams BaCl}_2 \text{ needed}$$

74.   a. $UO_2(s) + 4HF(aq) \rightarrow UF_4(aq) + 2H_2O(l)$

    One molecule (formula unit) of uranium(IV) oxide will combine with four molecules of hydrofluoric acid, producing one uranium(IV) fluoride molecule and two water molecules. One mole of uranium(IV) oxide will combine with four moles of hydrofluoric acid to produce one mole of uranium(IV) fluoride and two moles of water.

    b. $2NaC_2H_3O_2(aq) + H_2SO_4(aq) \rightarrow Na_2SO_4(aq) + 2HC_2H_3O_2(aq)$

    Two molecules (formula units) of sodium acetate react exactly with one molecule of sulfuric acid, producing one molecule (formula unit) of sodium sulfate and two molecules of acetic acid. Two moles of sodium acetate will combine with one mole of sulfuric acid, producing one mole of sodium sulfate and two moles of acetic acid.

    c. $Mg(s) + 2HCl(aq) \rightarrow MgCl_2(aq) + H_2(g)$

One magnesium atom will react with two hydrochloric acid molecules (formula units) to produce one molecule (formula unit) of magnesium chloride and one molecule of hydrogen gas. One mole of magnesium will combine with two moles of hydrochloric acid, producing one mole of magnesium chloride and one mole of gaseous hydrogen.

    d. $B_2O_3(s) + 3H_2O(l) \rightarrow 2B(OH)_3(aq)$

One molecule of diboron trioxide will react exactly with three molecules of water, producing two molecules of boron trihydroxide (boric acid). One mole of diboron trioxide will combine with three moles of water to produce two moles of boron trihydroxide (boric acid).

76.   For O_2: $\left(\dfrac{5 \text{ mol } O_2}{1 \text{ mol } C_3H_8} \right)$ For CO_2: $\left(\dfrac{3 \text{ mol } CO_2}{1 \text{ mol } C_3H_8} \right)$ For H_2O: $\left(\dfrac{4 \text{ mol } H_2O}{1 \text{ mol } C_3H_8} \right)$

78.   a. $NH_3(g) + HCl(g) \rightarrow NH_4Cl(s)$

molar mass of NH_3 = 17.01 g

$$1.00 \text{ g } NH_3 \times \frac{1 \text{ mol}}{17.01 \text{ g}} = 0.0588 \text{ mol } NH_3$$

$$0.0588 \text{ mol } NH_3 \times \frac{1 \text{ mol } NH_4Cl}{1 \text{ mol } NH_3} = 0.0588 \text{ mol } NH_4Cl$$

    b. $CaO(s) + CO_2(g) \rightarrow CaCO_3(s)$

molar mass CaO = 56.08 g

$$1.00 \text{ g } CaO \times \frac{1 \text{ mol}}{56.08 \text{ g}} = 0.0178 \text{ mol } CaO$$

$$0.0178 \text{ mol } CaO \times \frac{1 \text{ mol } CaCO_3}{1 \text{ mol } CaO} = 0.0178 \text{ mol } CaCO_3$$

    c. $4Na(s) + O_2(g) \rightarrow 2Na_2O(s)$

molar mass Na = 22.99 g

$$1.00 \text{ g } Na \times \frac{1 \text{ mol}}{22.99 \text{ g}} = 0.0435 \text{ mol } Na$$

$$0.0435 \text{ mol } Na \times \frac{2 \text{ mol } Na_2O}{4 \text{ mol } Na} = 0.0217 \text{ mol } Na_2O$$

    d. $2P(s) + 3Cl_2(g) \rightarrow 2PCl_3(l)$

molar mass P = 30.97 g

$$1.00 \text{ g } P \times \frac{1 \text{ mol}}{30.97 \text{ g}} = 0.0323 \text{ mol } P$$

$$0.0323 \text{ mol } P \times \frac{2 \text{ mol } PCl_3}{2 \text{ mol } P} = 0.0323 \text{ mol } PCl_3$$

80. a. molar mass HNO_3 = 63.0 g

$$5.0 \text{ mol } HNO_3 \times \frac{63.0 \text{ g}}{1 \text{ mol}} = 3.2 \times 10^2 \text{ g } HNO_3$$

b. molar mass Hg = 200.6 g

$$0.000305 \text{ mol Hg} \times \frac{200.6 \text{ g}}{1 \text{ mol}} = 0.0612 \text{ g Hg}$$

c. molar mass K_2CrO_4 = 194.2 g

$$2.31 \times 10^{-5} \text{ mol } K_2CrO_4 \times \frac{194.2 \text{ g}}{1 \text{ mol}} = 4.49 \times 10^{-3} \text{ g } K_2CrO_4$$

d. molar mass $AlCl_3$ = 133.3 g

$$10.5 \text{ mol } AlCl_3 \times \frac{133.3 \text{ g}}{1 \text{ mol}} = 1.40 \times 10^3 \text{ g } AlCl_3$$

e. molar mass SF_6 = 146.1 g

$$4.9 \times 10^4 \text{ mol } SF_6 \times \frac{146.1 \text{ g}}{1 \text{ mol}} = 7.2 \times 10^6 \text{ g } SF_6$$

f. molar mass NH_3 = 17.01 g

$$125 \text{ mol } NH_3 \times \frac{17.01 \text{ g}}{1 \text{ mol}} = 2.13 \times 10^3 \text{ g } NH_3$$

g. molar mass Na_2O_2 = 77.98 g

$$0.01205 \text{ mol } Na_2O_2 \times \frac{77.98 \text{ g}}{1 \text{ mol}} = 0.9397 \text{ g } Na_2O_2$$

82. $2SO_2(g) + O_2(g) \rightarrow 2SO_3(g)$

molar masses: SO_2, 64.07 g; SO_3, 80.07 g; 150 kg = 1.5×10^5 g

$$1.5 \times 10^5 \text{ g } SO_2 \times \frac{1 \text{ mol}}{64.07 \text{ g}} = 2.34 \times 10^3 \text{ mol } SO_2$$

$$2.34 \times 10^3 \text{ mol } SO_2 \times \frac{2 \text{ mol } SO_3}{2 \text{ mol } SO_2} = 2.34 \times 10^3 \text{ mol } SO_3$$

$$2.34 \times 10^3 \text{ mol } SO_3 \times \frac{80.07 \text{ g}}{1 \text{ mol}} = 1.9 \times 10^5 \text{ g } SO_3 = 1.9 \times 10^2 \text{ kg } SO_3$$

84. $2Na_2O_2(s) + 2H_2O(l) \rightarrow 4NaOH(aq) + O_2(g)$

molar masses: Na_2O_2, 77.98 g; O_2, 32.00 g

$$3.25 \text{ g } Na_2O_2 \times \frac{1 \text{ mol}}{77.98 \text{ g}} = 0.0417 \text{ mol } Na_2O_2$$

$$0.0417 \text{ mol } Na_2O_2 \times \frac{1 \text{ mol } O_2}{2 \text{ mol } Na_2O_2} = 0.0209 \text{ mol } O_2$$

$$0.0209 \text{ mol } O_2 \times \frac{32.00 \text{ g}}{1 \text{ mol}} = 0.667 \text{ g } O_2$$

86. $Zn(s) + 2HCl(aq) \rightarrow ZnCl_2(aq) + H_2(g)$

molar masses: Zn, 65.38 g; H_2, 2.016 g

$$2.50 \text{ g Zn} \times \frac{1 \text{ mol}}{65.38 \text{ g}} = 0.03824 \text{ mol Zn}$$

$$0.03824 \text{ mol Zn} \times \frac{1 \text{ mol } H_2}{1 \text{ mol Zn}} = 0.03824 \text{ mol } H_2$$

$$0.03824 \text{ mol } H_2 \times \frac{2.016 \text{ g}}{1 \text{ mol}} = 0.0771 \text{ g } H_2$$

88.   a. $2Na(s) + Br_2(l) \rightarrow 2NaBr(s)$

molar masses: Na, 22.99 g; Br_2, 159.8 g; NaBr, 102.9 g

$$5.0 \text{ g Na} \times \frac{1 \text{ mol}}{22.99 \text{ g}} = 0.2175 \text{ mol Na}$$

$$5.0 \text{ g } Br_2 \times \frac{1 \text{ mol}}{159.8 \text{ g}} = 0.03129 \text{ mol } Br_2$$

Intuitively, we would suspect that Br_2 is the limiting reactant, because there is much less Br_2 than Na on a mole basis. To *prove* that Br_2 is the limiting reactant, the following calculation is needed:

$$0.03129 \text{ mol } Br_2 \times \frac{2 \text{ mol Na}}{1 \text{ mol } Br_2} = 0.06258 \text{ mol Na}.$$

Clearly, there is more Na than this present, so Br_2 limits the reaction extent and the amount of NaBr formed.

$$0.03129 \text{ mol } Br_2 \times \frac{2 \text{ mol NaBr}}{1 \text{ mol } Br_2} = 0.06258 \text{ mol NaBr}$$

$$0.06258 \text{ mol NaBr} \times \frac{102.9 \text{ g}}{1 \text{ mol}} = 6.4 \text{ g NaBr}$$

b. $Zn(s) + CuSO_4(aq) \rightarrow ZnSO_4(aq) + Cu(s)$

molar masses: Zn, 65.38 g; Cu, 63.55 g; $ZnSO_4$, 161.5 g; $CuSO_4$, 159.6 g

$$5.0 \text{ g Zn} \times \frac{1 \text{ mol}}{65.38 \text{ g}} = 0.07648 \text{ mol Zn}$$

$$5.0 \text{ g } CuSO_4 \times \frac{1 \text{ mol}}{159.6 \text{ g}} = 0.03132 \text{ mol } CuSO_4$$

As the coefficients of Zn and $CuSO_4$ are the *same* in the balanced chemical equation, an equal number of moles of Zn and $CuSO_4$ would be needed for complete reaction. There is less $CuSO_4$ present, so $CuSO_4$ must be the limiting reactant.

$$0.03132 \text{ mol CuSO}_4 \times \frac{1 \text{ mol ZnSO}_4}{1 \text{ mol CuSO}_4} = 0.03132 \text{ mol ZnSO}_4$$

$$0.03132 \text{ mol ZnSO}_4 \times \frac{161.5 \text{ g}}{1 \text{ mol}} = 5.1 \text{ g ZnSO}_4$$

$$0.03132 \text{ mol CuSO}_4 \times \frac{1 \text{ mol Cu}}{1 \text{ mol CuSO}_4} = 0.03132 \text{ mol Cu}$$

$$0.03132 \text{ mol Cu} \times \frac{63.55 \text{ g}}{1 \text{ mol}} = 2.0 \text{ g Cu}$$

c. $NH_4Cl(aq) + NaOH(aq) \rightarrow NH_3(g) + H_2O(l) + NaCl(aq)$

molar masses: NH_4Cl, 53.49 g; NaOH, 40.00 g; NH_3, 17.03 g; H_2O, 18.02 g; NaCl, 58.44 g

$$5.0 \text{ g NH}_4Cl \times \frac{1 \text{ mol}}{53.49 \text{ g}} = 0.09348 \text{ mol NH}_4Cl$$

$$5.0 \text{ g NaOH} \times \frac{1 \text{ mol}}{40.00 \text{ g}} = 0.1250 \text{ mol NaOH}$$

As the coefficients of NH_4Cl and NaOH are both *one* in the balanced chemical equation for the reaction, an equal number of moles of NH_4Cl and NaOH would be needed for complete reaction. There is less NH_4Cl present, so NH_4Cl must be the limiting reactant.

As the coefficients of the products in the balanced chemical equation are also all *one*, if 0.09348 mol of NH_4Cl (the limiting reactant) reacts completely, then 0.09348 mol of each product will be formed.

$$0.09348 \text{ mol NH}_3 \times \frac{17.03 \text{ g}}{1 \text{ mol}} = 1.6 \text{ g NH}_3$$

$$0.09348 \text{ mol H}_2O \times \frac{18.02 \text{ g}}{1 \text{ mol}} = 1.7 \text{ g H}_2O$$

$$0.09348 \text{ mol NaCl} \times \frac{58.44 \text{ g}}{1 \text{ mol}} = 5.5 \text{ g NaCl}$$

d. $Fe_2O_3(s) + 3CO(g) \rightarrow 2Fe(s) + 3CO_2(g)$

molar masses: Fe_2O_3, 159.7 g; CO, 28.01 g; Fe, 55.85 g; CO_2, 44.01 g

$$5.0 \text{ g Fe}_2O_3 \times \frac{1 \text{ mol}}{159.7 \text{ g}} = 0.03131 \text{ mol Fe}_2O_3$$

$$5.0 \text{ g CO} \times \frac{1 \text{ mol}}{28.01 \text{ g}} = 0.1785 \text{ mol CO}$$

Because there is considerably less Fe_2O_3 than CO on a mole basis, let's see if Fe_2O_3 is the limiting reactant.

$$0.03131 \text{ mol Fe}_2O_3 \times \frac{3 \text{ mol CO}}{1 \text{ mol Fe}_2O_3} = 0.09393 \text{ mol CO}$$

As there is 0.1785 mol of CO present, but we have determined that only 0.09393 mol CO would be needed to react with all the Fe_2O_3 present, then Fe_2O_3 must be the limiting reactant. CO is present in excess.

$$0.03131 \text{ mol Fe}_2O_3 \times \frac{2 \text{ mol Fe}}{1 \text{ mol Fe}_2O_3} \times \frac{55.85 \text{ g Fe}}{1 \text{ mol Fe}} = 3.5 \text{ g Fe}$$

$$0.03131 \text{ mol Fe}_2O_3 \times \frac{3 \text{ mol CO}_2}{1 \text{ mol Fe}_2O_3} \times \frac{44.01 \text{ g CO}_2}{1 \text{ mol CO}_2} = 4.1 \text{ g CO}_2$$

90. $N_2H_4(l) + O_2(g) \rightarrow N_2(g) + 2H_2O(g)$

molar masses: N_2H_4, 32.05 g; O_2, 32.00 g; N_2, 28.02 g; H_2O, 18.02 g

$$20.0 \text{ g N}_2H_4 \times \frac{1 \text{ mol}}{32.05 \text{ g}} = 0.624 \text{ mol N}_2H_4$$

$$20.0 \text{ g O}_2 \times \frac{1 \text{ mol}}{32.00 \text{ g}} = 0.625 \text{ mol O}_2$$

The two reactants are present in nearly the required ratio for complete reaction (due to the 1:1 stoichiometry of the reaction and the very similar molar masses of the substances). We will consider N_2H_4 as the limiting reactant in the following calculations.

$$0.624 \text{ mol N}_2H_4 \times \frac{1 \text{ mol N}_2}{1 \text{ mol N}_2H_4} \times \frac{28.02 \text{ g N}_2}{1 \text{ mol N}_2} = 17.5 \text{ g N}_2$$

$$0.624 \text{ mol N}_2H_4 \times \frac{2 \text{ mol H}_2O}{1 \text{ mol N}_2H_4} \times \frac{18.02 \text{ g H}_2O}{1 \text{ mol H}_2O} = 22.5 \text{ g H}_2O$$

92. $12.5 \text{ g theory} \times \dfrac{40 \text{ g actual}}{100 \text{ g theory}} = 5.0 \text{ g}$

Chapters 8 and 9

2.   On a microscopic basis, one mole of a substance represents Avogadro's number (6.022×10^{23}) of individual units (atoms or molecules) of the substance. On a macroscopic, more practical basis, one mole of a substance represents the amount of substance present when the molar mass of the substance in grams is taken (for example 12.01 g of carbon will be one mole of carbon). Chemists have chosen these definitions so that there will be a simple relationship between measurable amounts of substances (grams) and the actual number of atoms or molecules present, and so that the number of particles present in samples of *different* substances can easily be compared. For example, it is known that carbon and oxygen react by the reaction

$$C(s) + O_2(g) \rightarrow CO_2(g).$$

Chemists understand this equation to mean that one carbon atom reacts with one oxygen molecule to produce one molecule of carbon dioxide, and also that one mole (12.01 g) of carbon will react with one mole (32.00 g) of oxygen to produce one mole (44.01 g) of carbon dioxide.

4.   The molar mass of a compound is the mass in grams of one mole of the compound (6.022×10^{23} molecules of the compound), and is calculated by summing the average atomic masses of all the atoms present in a molecule of the compound. For example, a molecule of the compound H_3PO_4 contains three hydrogen atoms, one phosphorus atom, and four oxygen atoms: the molar mass is obtained by adding up the average atomic masses of these atoms: molar mass $H_3PO_4 = 3(1.008 \text{ g}) + 1(30.97 \text{ g}) + 4(16.00 \text{ g}) = 97.99 \text{ g}$

6.   The empirical formula of a compound represents the lowest ratio of the relative number of atoms of each type present in a molecule of the compound, whereas the molecular formula represents the actual number of atoms of each type present in a real molecule of the compound. For example, both acetylene (molecular formula C_2H_2) and benzene (molecular formula C_6H_6) have the same relative number of carbon and hydrogen atoms (one hydrogen for each carbon atom), and so have the same empirical formula (CH). Once the empirical formula of a compound has been determined, it is also necessary to determine the molar mass of the compound before the actual molecular formula can be calculated. As real molecules cannot contain fractional parts of atoms, the molecular formula is always a whole number multiple of the empirical formula. For the examples above, the molecular formula of acetylene is twice the empirical formula, and the molecular formula of benzene is six times the empirical formula (both factors are integers).

8.   In question 7, suppose we chose to calculate the percentage composition of phosphoric acid, H_3PO_4: 3.086% H, 31.60% P, and 65.31% O. We could convert this percentage composition data into "experimental" data by first choosing a mass of sample to be "analyzed", and then calculating what mass of each element is present in this size sample using the percentage of each element. For example, suppose we choose our sample to have a mass of 2.417 g. Then the masses of H, P, and O present in this sample would be given by the following:

$$\text{g H} = (2.417 \text{ g sample}) \times \frac{3.086 \text{ g H}}{100.0 \text{ g sample}} = 0.07459 \text{ g H}$$

$$g \ P \ = (2.417 \text{ g sample}) \times \frac{31.60 \text{ g P}}{100.0 \text{ g sample}} = 0.7638 \text{ g P}$$

$$g \ O \ = (2.417 \text{ g sample}) \times \frac{65.31 \text{ g O}}{100.0 \text{ g sample}} = 1.579 \text{ g O}$$

Note that $(0.07459 \text{ g} + 0.7638 \text{ g} + 1.579 \text{ g}) = 2.41739 = 2.417 \text{ g}$.

So our new problem could be worded as follows: "A 2.417 g sample of a compound has been analyzed and was found to contain 0.07459 g H, 0.7638 g of P, and 1.579 g of oxygen. Calculate the empirical formula of the compound".

$$\text{mol H} = (0.07459 \text{ g H}) \times \frac{1 \text{ mol H}}{1.008 \text{ g H}} = 0.07400 \text{ mol H}$$

$$\text{mol P} = (0.7638 \text{ g P}) \times \frac{1 \text{ mol P}}{30.97 \text{ g P}} = 0.02466 \text{ mol P}$$

$$\text{mol O} = (1.579 \text{ g O}) \times \frac{1 \text{ mol O}}{16.00 \text{ g O}} = 0.09869 \text{ mol O}$$

Dividing each of these numbers of moles by the smallest number of moles (0.02466 mol P) gives the following:

$$\frac{0.07400 \text{ mol H}}{0.02466} = 3.001 \text{ mol H}$$

$$\frac{0.02466 \text{ mol P}}{0.02466} = 1.000 \text{ mol P}$$

$$\frac{0.09869 \text{ mol O}}{0.02466} = 4.002 \text{ mol O}$$

The empirical formula is (not surprisingly) just H_3PO_4!

10. The mole ratios for a reaction are based on the *coefficients* of the balanced chemical equation for the reaction: these coefficients show in what proportions molecules (or moles of molecules) combine. For a given amount of propane, the following mole ratios could be constructed, which would enable you to calculate the number of moles of each product, or of the second reactant, that would be involved.

$$C_3H_8(g) + 5O_2(g) \rightarrow 3CO_2(g) + 4H_2O(g)$$

for O_2: $\dfrac{5 \text{ mol O}_2}{1 \text{ mol C}_3\text{H}_8}$; $0.55 \text{ mol C}_3\text{H}_8 \times \dfrac{5 \text{ mol O}_2}{1 \text{ mol C}_3\text{H}_8} = 2.8 \ (2.75) \text{ mol O}_2$

for CO_2: $\dfrac{3 \text{ mol CO}_2}{1 \text{ mol C}_3\text{H}_8}$; $0.55 \text{ mol C}_3\text{H}_8 \times \dfrac{3 \text{ mol CO}_2}{1 \text{ mol C}_3\text{H}_8} = 1.7 \ (1.65) \text{ mol CO}_2$

for H_2O: $\dfrac{4 \text{ mol H}_2\text{O}}{1 \text{ mol C}_3\text{H}_8}$; $0.55 \text{ mol C}_3\text{H}_8 \times \dfrac{4 \text{ mol H}_2\text{O}}{1 \text{ mol C}_3\text{H}_8} = 2.2 \text{ mol H}_2\text{O}$

12. Although we can calculate specifically the exact amounts of each reactant needed for a chemical reaction, oftentimes reaction mixtures are prepared using more or less arbitrary amounts of the

reagents. However, regardless of how much of each reagent may be used for a reaction, the substances still react stoichiometrically, according to the mole ratios derived from the balanced chemical equation for the reaction. When arbitrary amounts of reactants are used, there will be one reactant which, stoichiometrically, is present in the least amount. This substance is called the *limiting reactant* for the experiment. It is the limiting reactant that controls how much product is formed, regardless of how much of the other reactants are present. The limiting reactant limits the amount of product that can form in the experiment, because once the limiting reactant has reacted completely, the reaction must stop. We say that the other reactants in the experiment are present in excess, which means that a portion of these reactants will still be present unchanged after the reaction has ended and the limiting reactant has been used up completely.

14. The *theoretical yield* for an experiment is the mass of product calculated based on the limiting reactant for the experiment being completely consumed. The *actual yield* for an experiment is the mass of product actually collected by the experimenter. Obviously, any experiment is restricted by the skills of the experimenter and by the inherent limitations of the experimental method being used. For these reasons, the actual yield is often *less* than the theoretical yield (most scientific writers report the actual or percentage yield for their experiments as an indication of the usefulness of their experiments). Although one would expect that the actual yield should never be more than the theoretical yield, in real experiments, sometimes this happens: however, an actual yield greater than a theoretical yield is usually taken to mean that something is *wrong* in either the experiment (for example, impurities may be present, or the reaction may not occur as envisioned) or in the calculations.

16. $\%\text{ element X} = \dfrac{\text{mass of element X in compound}}{\text{molar mass of compound}} \times 100$

a.	92.26% C	b.	32.37% Na
c.	15.77% C	d.	20.24% Al
e.	88.82% Cu	f.	79.89% Cu
g.	71.06% Co	h.	40.00% C

18. a. molar masses: SiC, 40.10 g; SiCl₄, 169.9 g

$$12.5 \text{ g SiC} \times \frac{1 \text{ mol}}{40.10 \text{ g}} = 0.3117 \text{ mol SiC}$$

for SiCl₄: $0.3117 \text{ mol SiC} \times \dfrac{1 \text{ mol SiCl}_4}{1 \text{ mol SiC}} \times \dfrac{169.9 \text{ g SiCl}_4}{1 \text{ mol SiCl}_4} = 53.0 \text{ g SiCl}_4$

for C: $0.3117 \text{ mol SiC} \times \dfrac{1 \text{ mol C}}{1 \text{ mol SiC}} \times \dfrac{12.01 \text{ g C}}{1 \text{ mol C}} = 3.75 \text{ g C}$

   b. molar masses: Li₂O, 29.88 g; LiOH, 23.95 g

$$12.5 \text{ g Li}_2\text{O} \times \frac{1 \text{ mol}}{29.88 \text{ g}} = 0.4183 \text{ mol Li}_2\text{O}$$

$$0.4183 \text{ mol Li}_2\text{O} \times \frac{2 \text{ mol LiOH}}{1 \text{ mol Li}_2\text{O}} \times \frac{23.95 \text{ g LiOH}}{1 \text{ mol LiOH}} = 20.0 \text{ g LiOH}$$

c. molar masses: Na_2O_2, 77.98 g; NaOH, 40.00 g; O_2, 32.00 g

$$12.5 \text{ g} \times \frac{1 \text{ mol}}{77.98 \text{ g}} = 0.1603 \text{ mol } Na_2O_2$$

for NaOH: $0.1603 \text{ mol } Na_2O_2 \times \dfrac{4 \text{ mol NaOH}}{2 \text{ mol } Na_2O_2} \times \dfrac{40.00 \text{ g NaOH}}{1 \text{ mol NaOH}} = 12.8 \text{ g NaOH}$

for O_2: $0.1603 \text{ mol } Na_2O_2 \times \dfrac{1 \text{ mol } O_2}{2 \text{ mol } Na_2O_2} \times \dfrac{32.00 \text{ g } O_2}{1 \text{ mol } O_2} = 2.56 \text{ g } O_2$

d. molar masses: SnO_2, 150.7 g; Sn, 118.7 g; H_2O, 18.02 g

$$12.5 \text{ g } SnO_2 \times \frac{1 \text{ mol}}{150.7 \text{ g}} = 0.08295 \text{ mol } SnO_2$$

for Sn: $0.08295 \text{ mol } SnO_2 \times \dfrac{1 \text{ mol Sn}}{1 \text{ mol } SnO_2} \times \dfrac{118.7 \text{ g Sn}}{1 \text{ mol Sn}} = 9.84 \text{ g Sn}$

for H_2O: $0.08295 \text{ mol } SnO_2 \times \dfrac{2 \text{ mol } H_2O}{1 \text{ mol } SnO_2} \times \dfrac{18.02 \text{ g } H_2O}{1 \text{ mol } H_2O} = 2.99 \text{ g } H_2O$

20. molar masses: C, 12.01 g; CO, 28.01 g; CO_2, 44.01 g

$$5.00 \text{ g C} \times \frac{1 \text{ mol C}}{12.01 \text{ g C}} = 0.416 \text{ mol C}$$

for CO: $0.416 \text{ mol C} \times \dfrac{2 \text{ mol CO}}{2 \text{ mol C}} \times \dfrac{28.01 \text{ g CO}}{1 \text{ mol CO}} = 11.7 \text{ g CO}$

for CO_2: $0.416 \text{ mol C} \times \dfrac{1 \text{ mol } CO_2}{1 \text{ mol C}} \times \dfrac{44.01 \text{ g } CO_2}{1 \text{ mol } CO_2} = 18.3 \text{ g } CO_2$

CHAPTER 11

Modern Atomic Theory

2.   Rutherford's experiments determined that the atom had a nucleus containing positively-charged particles called protons and neutral particles called neutrons. He established that the nucleus was very small compared to the overall size of the atom. He was not able to determine where the electrons were in the atom or what they were doing.

4.   The different forms of electromagnetic radiation are similar in that they all exhibit the same type of wave-like behavior and are propagated through space at the same speed (the speed of light). The types of electromagnetic radiation differ in their frequency (and wavelength) and in the resulting amount of energy carried per photon.

6.   The *speed* of electromagnetic radiation represents how fast a given wave moves through space. The *frequency* of electromagnetic radiation represents how many complete cycles of the wave pass a given point per second. These two concepts are not the same.

8.   The greenhouse gases do not absorb light in the visible wavelengths, enabling this light to pass through the atmosphere and continue to warm the earth, keeping the earth much warmer than it would be without these gases. The earth, in turn, emits infrared radiation which is absorbed by the greenhouse gases and which is re-emitted in all directions. As we increase our use of fossil fuels, the level of CO_2 in the atmosphere is increasing gradually, but significantly. An increase in the level of CO_2 will warm the earth further, eventually changing the weather patterns on the earth's surface and melting the polar ice caps.

10. exactly equal to

12. A photon having an energy corresponding to the energy difference between the two states is emitted by an atom in an excited state when it returns to its ground state.

14. absorbs

16. When excited hydrogen atoms emit their excess energy, the photons of radiation emitted are always of exactly the same wavelength and energy. We consider this to mean that the hydrogen atom possesses only certain allowed energy states, and that the photons emitted correspond to the atom changing from one of these allowed energy states to another of the allowed energy state. The energy of the photon emitted corresponds to the energy difference in the allowed states. If the hydrogen atom did not possess discrete energy levels, then we would expect the photons emitted to have random wavelengths and energies.

18. The energy of an emitted photon is *identical* to the energy change within the atom that gave rise to the emitted photon.

20. Energy is emitted only at wavelengths corresponding to the specific transitions for the electron among the energy levels of hydrogen.

22.   The electron moves to an orbit farther from the nucleus of the atom.

24.   Bohr's theory *explained* the experimentally *observed* line spectrum of hydrogen *exactly*. Bohr's theory was ultimately discarded because when attempts were made to extend the theory to atoms other than hydrogen, the calculated properties did *not* correspond closely to experimental measurements.

26.   An orbit represents a definite, exact circular pathway around the nucleus in which an electron can be found. An orbital represents a region of space in which there is a high probability of finding the electron.

28.   The firefly analogy is intended to demonstrate the concept of a probability map for electron density. In the wave mechanical model of the atom, we cannot say specifically where the electron is in the atom, we can only say where there is a high probability of finding the electron. The analogy is to imagine a time-exposure photograph of a firefly in a closed room. Most of the time, the firefly will be found near the center of the room.

30.   Pictures we draw to represent orbitals should only be interpreted as probability maps. They are not meant to represent that the electron moves only on the surface of, or within, the region drawn in the picture. As the mathematical probability of finding the electron never actually becomes zero on moving outward from the nucleus, scientists have decided that pictures of orbitals should represent a 90% probability that the electron will be found inside the region depicted in the drawing (for 100% probability, the orbital would have to encompass all space).

32.   The p orbitals, in general, have two lobes and are sometimes described as having a "dumbbell" shape. The $2p$ and $3p$ orbitals are similar in shape, and in fact there are three equivalent $2p$ or $3p$ orbitals in the $2p$ or $3p$ subshell. The orbitals differ in size, mean distance from the nucleus, and energy.

34. $n = 1$

36.

Value of n	Possible subshells
1	$1s$
2	$2s, 2p$
3	$3s, 3p, 3d$
4	$4s, 4p, 4d, 4f$

38.   Electrons have an intrinsic spin (they spin on their own axes). Geometrically, there are only two senses possible for spin (clockwise or counter-clockwise). This means only two electrons can occupy an orbital, with the opposite sense or direction of spin. This idea is called the Pauli Exclusion Principle.

40.   increases; as you move out from the nucleus, there is more space and room for more sublevels.

42.   opposite

44.   Choices b and c are possible; choice a is not possible because the f subshells do not begin until the $n = 4$ orbit; choice d is not possible because the p subshells do not begin until the $n = 2$ orbit.

46.   When a hydrogen atom is in its ground state, the electron is found in the $1s$ orbital. The $1s$ orbital has the lowest energy of all the possible hydrogen orbitals.

48.   The elements in a given vertical column of the periodic table have the same valence electron configuration. Having the same valence electron configuration causes the elements in a given group to have similar chemical properties.

50.   Just count the electrons to get the atomic number of the element.

    a.   silicon

    b.   beryllium

    c.   neon

    d.   argon

52.   Just count the electrons to get the atomic number of the element.

    a.   selenium

    b.   scandium

    c.   sulfur

    d.   iodine

54.   a. $1s(\uparrow\downarrow)\ 2s(\uparrow\downarrow)\ 2p(\uparrow\downarrow)(\uparrow\downarrow)(\uparrow\downarrow)\ 3s(\uparrow\downarrow)$

    b. $1s(\uparrow\downarrow)\ 2s(\uparrow\downarrow)\ 2p(\uparrow\downarrow)(\uparrow\downarrow)(\uparrow\downarrow)\ 3s(\uparrow\downarrow)\ 3p(\uparrow\downarrow)(\uparrow\downarrow)(\uparrow\downarrow)$

    c. $1s(\uparrow\downarrow)\ 2s(\uparrow\ )$

    d. $1s(\uparrow\downarrow)\ 2s(\uparrow\downarrow)\ 2p(\uparrow\downarrow)(\uparrow\downarrow)(\uparrow\downarrow)\ 3s(\uparrow\downarrow)\ 3p(\uparrow\downarrow)(\uparrow\downarrow)(\uparrow\downarrow)\ 4s(\uparrow\downarrow)$
        $3d(\uparrow\downarrow)(\uparrow\downarrow)(\uparrow\downarrow)(\uparrow\downarrow)(\uparrow\downarrow)\ 4p(\uparrow\ )(\uparrow\ )(\uparrow\ )$

56.   Specific answers depend on student choice of elements. Any Group 1 element would have one valence electron. Any Group 3 element would have three valence electrons. Any Group 5 element would have five valence electrons. Any Group 7 element would have seven valence electrons.

58.   The properties of Rb and Sr suggest that they are members of Groups 1 and 2, respectively, and so must be filling the $5s$ orbital. The $5s$ orbital is lower in energy (and fills before) the $4d$ orbitals.

60.   a.   aluminum

    b.   potassium

    c.   bromine

    d.   tin

62.   a. $[Ne]\ 3s^2\ 3p^3$

    b. $[Ne]\ 3s^2\ 3p^5$

    c. $[Ne]\ 3s^2$

    d. $[Ar]\ 4s^2\ 3d^{10}$

64.   a.   one

       b.   two

       c.   zero

       d.   ten

66.   The *position* of the element (both in terms of vertical column and horizontal row) indicates which set of orbitals is being filled last.

       a. $5f$

       b. $5f$

       c. $4f$

       d. $6p$

68. $[Rn]\ 7s^2\ 5f^{14}\ 6d^6$

70.   The metallic elements *lose* electrons and form *positive* ions (cations); the nonmetallic elements *gain* electrons and form *negative* ions (anions). Remember that the electron itself is *negatively* charged.

72.   All exist as *diatomic* molecules (F_2, Cl_2, Br_2, I_2); all are *non*metals; all have relatively high electronegativities; all form 1- ions in reacting with metallic elements.

74.   Elements at the *left* of a period (horizontal row) lose electrons more readily; at the left of a period (given principal energy level) the nuclear charge is the smallest and the electrons are least tightly held.

76.   The elements of a given period (horizontal row) have valence electrons in the same principal energy level. Nuclear charge, however, increases across a period going from left to right. Atoms at the left side have smaller nuclear charges and hold onto their valence electrons less tightly.

78.   When substances absorb energy the electrons become excited (move to higher energy levels). Upon returning to the ground state, energy is released, some of which is in the visible spectrum. Since we see colors, this tells us that only *certain wavelengths* of light are released, which means that only *certain transitions* are allowed. This is what is meant by quantized energy levels. If all wavelengths of light were emitted we would see white light.

80.   Ionization energies decrease in going from top to bottom within a vertical group; ionization energies increase in going from left to right within a horizontal period.

       a.   Li

       b.   Ca

       c.   Cl

       d.   S

82. Atomic size increases in going from top to bottom within a vertical group; atomic size decreases in going from left to right within a horizontal period.

    a. Na

    b. S

    c. N

    d. F

84. speed of light

86. photons

88. quantized

90. orbital

92. transition metal

94. spins

96. a. $1s^2\, 2s^2\, 2p^6\, 3s^2\, 3p^6\, 4s^1$ [Ar] $4s^1$

    $1s(\uparrow\downarrow)\ 2s(\uparrow\downarrow)\ 2p(\uparrow\downarrow)(\uparrow\downarrow)(\uparrow\downarrow)\ 3s(\uparrow\downarrow)\ 3p(\uparrow\downarrow)(\uparrow\downarrow)(\uparrow\downarrow)\ 4s(\uparrow\ )$

    b. $1s^2\, 2s^2\, 2p^6\, 3s^2\, 3p^6\, 4s^2\, 3d^2$ [Ar] $4s^2\, 3d^2$

    $1s(\uparrow\downarrow)\ 2s(\uparrow\downarrow)\ 2p(\uparrow\downarrow)(\uparrow\downarrow)(\uparrow\downarrow)\ 3s(\uparrow\downarrow)\ 3p(\uparrow\downarrow)(\uparrow\downarrow)(\uparrow\downarrow)\ 4s(\uparrow\downarrow)$
    $3d(\uparrow\ )(\uparrow\ )(\ )(\ )(\ )$

    c. $1s^2\, 2s^2\, 2p^6\, 3s^2\, 3p^2$ [Ne] $3s^2\, 3p^2$

    $1s(\uparrow\downarrow)\ 2s(\uparrow\downarrow)\ 2p(\uparrow\downarrow)(\uparrow\downarrow)(\uparrow\downarrow)\ 3s(\uparrow\downarrow)\ 3p(\uparrow\ )(\uparrow\ )(\ )$

    d. $1s^2\, 2s^2\, 2p^6\, 3s^2\, 3p^6\, 4s^2\, 3d^6$ [Ar] $4s^2\, 3d^6$

    $1s(\uparrow\downarrow)\ 2s(\uparrow\downarrow)\ 2p(\uparrow\downarrow)(\uparrow\downarrow)(\uparrow\downarrow)\ 3s(\uparrow\downarrow)\ 3p(\uparrow\downarrow)(\uparrow\downarrow)(\uparrow\downarrow)\ 4s(\uparrow\downarrow)$
    $3d(\uparrow\downarrow)(\uparrow\ )(\uparrow\ )(\uparrow\ )(\uparrow\ )$

    e. $1s^2\, 2s^2\, 2p^6\, 3s^2\, 3p^6\, 4s^2\, 3d^{10}$ [Ar] $4s^2\, 3d^{10}$

    $1s(\uparrow\downarrow)\ 2s(\uparrow\downarrow)\ 2p(\uparrow\downarrow)(\uparrow\downarrow)(\uparrow\downarrow)\ 3s(\uparrow\downarrow)\ 3p(\uparrow\downarrow)(\uparrow\downarrow)(\uparrow\downarrow)\ 4s(\uparrow\downarrow)$
    $3d(\uparrow\downarrow)(\uparrow\downarrow)(\uparrow\downarrow)(\uparrow\downarrow)(\uparrow\downarrow)$

98. a. ns^2

    b. $ns^2\, np^5$

    c. $ns^2\, np^4$

    d. ns^1

    e. $ns^2\, np^4$

100.   a. $\lambda = \dfrac{h}{mv}$

            $\lambda = \dfrac{6.63 \times 10^{-34} \text{ J s}}{(9.1 \times 10^{-31} \text{kg})[0.90 \times (3.00 \times 10^{8} \text{ m s}^{-1})}$

            $\lambda = 2.7 \times 10^{-12}$ m (0.0027 nm)

   b. 4.4×10^{-34} m

   c. 2×10^{-35} m

        The wavelengths for the ball and the person are *infinitesimally small*, whereas the wavelength for the electron is nearly the same order of magnitude as the diameter of a typical atom.

102.   Light is emitted from the hydrogen atom only at certain fixed wavelengths. If the energy levels of hydrogen were *continuous*, a hydrogen atom would emit energy at all possible wavelengths.

104.   The third principal energy level of hydrogen is divided into *three* sublevels (3s, 3p, and 3d); there is a *single* 3s orbital; there is a set of *three* 3p orbitals; there is a set of *five* 3d orbitals. See Figures 11.21-11.24 for the shapes of these orbitals.

106.   Answer depends on student choice of examples.

108.   a. $1s^2 \, 2s^2 \, 2p^6 \, 3s^2 \, 3p^6 \, 4s^2 \, 3d^{10} \, 4p^5$

   b. $1s^2 \, 2s^2 \, 2p^6 \, 3s^2 \, 3p^6 \, 4s^2 \, 3d^{10} \, 4p^6 \, 5s^2 \, 4d^{10} \, 5p^6$

   c. $1s^2 \, 2s^2 \, 2p^6 \, 3s^2 \, 3p^6 \, 4s^2 \, 3d^{10} \, 4p^6 \, 5s^2 \, 4d^{10} \, 5p^6 \, 6s^2$

   d. $1s^2 \, 2s^2 \, 2p^6 \, 3s^2 \, 3p^6 \, 4s^2 \, 3d^{10} \, 4p^4$

110.   a.   five (2s, 2p)

   b.   seven (3s, 3p)

   c.   one (3s)

   d.   three (3s, 3p)

112.   a.   [Kr] $5s^2 \, 4d^2$

   b.   [Kr] $5s^2 \, 4d^{10} \, 5p^5$

   c.   [Ar] $4s^2 \, 3d^{10} \, 4p^2$

   d.   [Xe] $6s^1$

114.   a.   Se

   b.   Se

   c.   Rb

   d.   V

116.   metals, low; nonmetals, high

118.   Atomic size increases in going from top to bottom within a vertical group; atomic size decreases in going from left to right within a horizontal period.

  a.   Ca

  b.   P

  c.   K

CHAPTER 12

Chemical Bonding

2.   The *bond energy* represents the energy required to break a chemical bond.

4.   A covalent bond represents the *sharing* of pairs of electrons between nuclei.

6.   In H_2 and HF, the bonding is covalent in nature, with an electron pair being shared between the atoms. In H_2, the two atoms are identical (the sharing is equal); in HF, the two atoms are different (the sharing is unequal) and as a result the bond is polar. Both of these are in marked contrast to the situation in NaF: NaF is an ionic compound—an electron has been completely transferred from sodium to fluorine, producing separate ions.

8.   A bond is polar if the centers of positive and negative charge do not coincide at the same point. The bond has a negative end and a positive end. Polar bonds will exist in any molecule with nonidentical bonded atoms (although the molecule, as a whole, may not be polar if the bond dipoles cancel each other). Two simple examples are HF and HCl: in both cases, the negative center of charge is closer to the halogen atom.

10.   The level of polarity in a polar covalent bond is determined by the difference in electronegativity of the atoms in the bond.

12.   a.   I is most electronegative, Rb is least electronegative

        b.   Mg is most electronegative, Ca and Sr have similar electronegativities

        c.   Br is most electronegative, K is least electronegative

14.   Generally, covalent bonds between atoms of *different* elements are *polar*.

        a.   ionic

        b.   polar covalent

        c.   covalent

16.   For a bond to be polar covalent, the atoms involved in the bond must have different electronegativities (must be of different elements).

        a.   nonpolar covalent (atoms of the same element)

        b.   nonpolar covalent (atoms of the same element)

        c.   polar covalent (atoms of different elements)

        d.   polar covalent (atoms of different elements)

18. The *degree* of polarity of a polar covalent bond is indicated by the magnitude of the difference in electronegativities of the elements involved: the larger the difference in electronegativity, the more polar the bond. Electronegativity differences are given in parentheses below:

    a. O–Cl (0.5); O–Br(0.7); the O–Br bond is more polar

    b. N–O (0.5); N–F (1.0); the N–F bond is more polar

    c. P–S (0.4); P–O (1.4); the P–O bond is more polar

    d. H–O (1.4); H–N (0.9); the H–O bond is more polar

20. The greater the electronegativity difference between two atoms, the more ionic will be the bond between those two atoms.

    a. Ca–Cl

    b. Ba–Cl

    c. Fe–I

    d. Be–F

22. The presence of strong bond dipoles and a large overall dipole moment in water make it a polar substance overall. Among the properties of water dependent on its dipole moment are its freezing point, melting point, vapor pressure, and its ability to dissolve many substances.

24. In a diatomic molecule containing two different elements, the more electronegative atom will be the negative end of the molecule, and the *less* electronegative atom will be the positive end.

    a. H

    b. Cl

    c. I

26. In the figures, the arrow points toward the more electronegative atom.

    a. $\delta+$ S→O $\delta-$

    b. $\delta+$ S→N $\delta-$

    c. $\delta+$ S→F $\delta-$

    d. $\delta+$ S→Cl $\delta-$

28. In the figures, the arrow points toward the more electronegative atom.

    a. $\delta+$ H→C $\delta-$

    b. $\delta+$ N→O $\delta-$

    c. $\delta+$ S→N $\delta-$

    d. $\delta+$ C→N $\delta-$

30. preceding

32.   Atoms in covalent molecules gain a configuration like that of a noble gas by sharing one or more pairs of electrons between atoms: such shared pairs of electrons "belong" to each of the atoms of the bond at the same time. In ionic bonding, one atom completely gives over one or more electrons to another atom, and the resulting ions behave independently of one another.

34.   a. Br^-, Kr (Br has one electron less than Kr)

      b. Cs^+, Xe (Cs has one electron more than Xe)

      c. P^{3-}, Ar (P has three fewer electrons than Ar)

      d. S^{2-}, Ar (S has two fewer electrons than Ar)

36.   Atoms or ions with the same number of electrons are said to be *isoelectronic*.

      a. F^-, O^{2-}, N^{3-}

      b. Cl^-, S^{2-}, P^{3-}

      c. F^-, O^{2-}, N^{3-}

      d. Br^-, Se^{2-}, As^{3-}

38.   a. $AlBr_3$: Al has three electrons more than a noble gas; Br has one electron less than a noble gas.

      b. Al_2O_3: Al has three electrons more than a noble gas; O has two fewer electrons than a noble gas.

      c.   AlP: Al has three electrons more than a noble gas; P has three fewer electrons than a noble gas.

      d. AlH_3: Al has three electrons more than a noble gas; H has one electron less than a noble gas.

40.   There are many examples possible. Listed below are a few compounds that fit each situation.

      a.   LiF: Li^+, [He]; F^-, [Ne]

      b.   NaF: Na^+, [Ne]; F^-, [Ne]

      c.   LiCl: Li^+, [He]; Cl^-, [Ar]

      d.   NaCl: Na^+, [Ne]; Cl^-, [Ar]

42.   An ionic solid such as NaCl consists of an array of alternating positively– and negatively–charged ions: that is, each positive ion has as its nearest neighbors a group of negative ions, and each negative ion has a group of positive ions surrounding it. In most ionic solids, the ions are packed as tightly as possible.

44.   In forming an anion, an atom gains additional electrons in its outermost (valence) shell. Additional electrons in the valence shell increases the repulsive forces between electrons, so the outermost shell becomes larger to accommodate this.

46.   Relative ionic sizes are given in Figure 12.9. Within a given horizontal row of the periodic chart, negative ions tend to be larger than positive ions because the negative ions contain a larger number of electrons in the valence shell. Within a vertical group of the periodic table, ionic size increases from top to bottom. In general, positive ions are smaller than the atoms they come from, whereas negative ions are larger than the atoms they come from.

    a. F^-

    b. Cl^-

    c.   Ca

    d. I^-

48.   Relative ionic sizes are given in Figure 12.9. Within a given horizontal row of the periodic chart, negative ions tend to be larger than positive ions because the negative ions contain a larger number of electrons in the valence shell. Within a vertical group of the periodic table, ionic size increases from top to bottom. In general, positive ions are smaller than the atoms they come from, whereas negative ions are larger than the atoms they come from.

    a.   I

    b. F^-

    c. F^-

50.   When atoms form covalent bonds, they try to attain a valence electronic configuration similar to that of the following noble gas element. When the elements in the first few horizontal rows of the periodic table form covalent bonds, they will attempt to gain configurations similar to the noble gases helium (2 valence electrons, duet rule), and neon and argon (8 valence electrons, octet rule).

52.   These elements attain a total of eight valence electrons, making the valence electron configurations similar to those of the noble gases Ne and Ar.

54.   When two atoms in a molecule are connected by a triple bond, the atoms share three pairs of electrons (6 electrons) in completing their outermost shells. A simple molecule containing a triple bond is acetylene, C_2H_2 (H:C:::C:H).

56.   The Group in which a representative element is found indicates the number of valence electrons.

    a.   Mg:

    b.   :B̈r·

    c.   :S̈·

    d.   :S̈i

58.   a.   each boron provides 3; each oxygen provides 6; total valence electrons = 24

    b.   carbon provides 4; each oxygen provides 6; total valence electrons = 16

       c.   each carbon provides 4; each hydrogen provides 1; oxygen provides 6; total valence electrons = 20

       d.   N provides 5; each oxygen provides 6; total valence electrons = 17

60.   a.   Each hydrogen provides 1 valence electron; total valence electrons = 2

               H—H

       b.   Hydrogen provides 1 valence electron; chlorine provides 7 valence electrons; total valence electrons = 8

               H—$\ddot{\text{C}}$l:

       c.   Carbon provides 4 valence electrons; each fluorine provides 7 valence electrons; total valence electrons = 32

$$:\ddot{\text{F}}: \\ | \\ :\ddot{\text{F}}\text{—C—}\ddot{\text{F}}: \\ | \\ :\ddot{\text{F}}:$$

       d.   Each carbon provides 4 valence electrons; each fluorine provides 7 valence electrons; total valence electrons = 50

$$:\ddot{\text{F}}: \quad :\ddot{\text{F}}: \\ | \qquad | \\ :\ddot{\text{F}}\text{—C—C—}\ddot{\text{F}}: \\ | \qquad | \\ :\ddot{\text{F}}: \quad :\ddot{\text{F}}:$$

62.   a.   P provides 5 valence electrons. Each Cl provides 7 valence electrons.
Total valence electrons = 26

$$:\ddot{\text{C}}\text{l——}\ddot{\text{P}}\text{——}\ddot{\text{C}}\text{l:} \\ | \\ :\ddot{\text{C}}\text{l:}$$

       b.   C provides 4 valence electrons. Each Cl provides 7 valence electrons. H provides 1 valence electron.
Total valence electrons = 26

$$\text{H} \\ | \\ :\ddot{\text{C}}\text{l——C——}\ddot{\text{C}}\text{l:} \\ | \\ :\ddot{\text{C}}\text{l:}$$

c.   Each C provides 4 valence electrons. Each H provides 1 valence electron. Each Cl
provides 7 valence electrons
Total valence electrons = 26

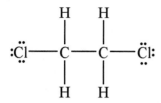

d.   Each N provides 5 valence electrons. Each H provides 1 valence electron.
Total valence electrons = 14

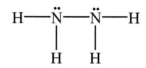

64.   C provides 4 valence electrons. Each oxygen provides 6 valence electrons. Having only 16 total
valence electrons requires multiple bonding in the molecule.

$$:O{\equiv}C-\ddot{\underset{..}{O}}: \quad\longleftrightarrow\quad \ddot{\underset{..}{O}}{=}C{=}\ddot{\underset{..}{O}} \quad\longleftrightarrow\quad :\ddot{\underset{..}{O}}-C{\equiv}O:$$

66.   a.   Cl provides 7 valence electrons. Each O provides 6 valence electrons.   The 1– charge
means 1 additional electron. Total valence electrons = 26

$$\left[\begin{array}{c} :\ddot{O}: \\ | \\ :\ddot{\underset{..}{O}}-\underset{}{Cl}-\ddot{\underset{..}{O}}: \end{array}\right]^{1-}$$

b.   Each O provides 6 valence electrons.   The 2– charge means two additional valence
electrons. Total valence electrons = 14

$$\left[\ :\ddot{\underset{..}{O}}-\ddot{\underset{..}{O}}:\ \right]^{2-}$$

c.   Each C provides 4 valence electrons. Each H provides 1 valence electron. Each O
provides 6 valence electrons.   The 1– charge means 1 additional valence electron.
Total valence electrons = 24

$$\left[\begin{array}{c} H \quad :\ddot{O}: \\ | \quad\quad || \\ H-C-C-\ddot{\underset{..}{O}}: \\ | \\ H \end{array}\right]^{1-} \left[\begin{array}{c} H \quad :\ddot{O}: \\ | \quad\quad | \\ H-C-C{=}\ddot{\underset{..}{O}} \\ | \\ H \end{array}\right]^{1-}$$

68.   a.   C provides 4 valence electrons. Each O provides 6 valence electrons. The 2– charge means two additional valence electrons.
Total valence electrons = 24

b.   Each H provides 1 valence electron. N provides 5 valence electrons. The 1+ charge means one less valence electron.
Total valence electrons = 8

c.   Cl provides 7 valence electrons. O provides 6 valence electrons. The 1– charge means one additional valence electron. Total valence electrons = 14

70.   The geometric structure of NH_3 is that of a trigonal pyramid. The nitrogen atom of NH_3 is surrounded by four electron pairs (three are bonding, one is a lone pair). The H–N–H bond angle is somewhat less than 109.5° (due to the presence of the lone pair).

72.   The geometric structure of SiF_4 is that of a tetrahedron. The silicon atom of SiF_4 is surrounded by four bonding electron pairs. The F–Si–F bond angle is the characteristic angle of the tetrahedron, 109.5°.

74.   The general molecular structure of a molecule is determined by (1) *how many electron pairs* surround the central atom in the molecule, and (2) which of those electron pairs are used for *bonding* to the other atoms of the molecule. Nonbonding electron pairs on the central atom do, however, cause minor changes in the bond angles, compared to the ideal regular geometric structure.

76.   You will remember from high school geometry, that two points in space are all that is needed to define a straight line. A diatomic molecule represents two points (the nuclei of the atoms) in space.

78.   In NF_3, the nitrogen atom has *four* pairs of valence electrons, whereas in BF_3, there are only *three* pairs of valence electrons around the boron atom. The nonbonding electron pair on nitrogen in NF_3 pushes the three F atoms out of the plane of the N atom.

80.   a.   four electron pairs in a tetrahedral arrangement with some lone-pair distortion

        b.   four electron pairs in a tetrahedral arrangement with some lone-pair distortion

        c.   four electron pairs in a tetrahedral arrangement

82.   a.   trigonal pyramidal (there is a lone pair on N)

        b.   trigonal pyramidal (there is a lone pair on As)

        c.   non-linear, *V*-shaped (four electron pairs on O, but only two atoms are attached to O)

84.   a.   basically tetrahedral around the P atom (the hydrogen atoms are attached to two of the oxygen atoms and do not affect greatly the geometrical arrangement of the oxygen atoms around the phosphorus)

        b.   tetrahedral (4 electron pairs on Cl, and 4 atoms attached)

        c.   trigonal pyramidal (4 electron pairs on S, and 3 atoms attached)

86.   a.   approximately 109.5° (the molecule is *V*-shaped or nonlinear)

        b.   approximately 109.5° (the molecule is trigonal pyramidal)

        c.   109.5°

        d.   approximately 120° (the double bond makes the molecule flat)

88.   The bond angles would be expected to be 120° around the carbon atoms in the rings. We also expect 120° for the C–N–N and N–N–C bond angles. The double bonds influence the bond angles greatly, with each atom having only three "effective pairs" of electrons around the atom.

90.   double

92.   The bond with the larger electronegativity difference will be the more polar bond. See Figure 12.3 for electronegativities.

        a.   S–F

        b.   P–O

        c.   C–H

94.   The bond energy of a chemical bond is the quantity of energy required to break the bond and separate the atoms.

96.   In each case, the element *higher up* within a group on the periodic table has the higher electronegativity.

        a.   Be

        b.   N

        c.   F

98.   For a bond to be polar covalent, the atoms involved in the bond must have different electronegativities (must be of different elements).

    a.   polar covalent (different elements)

    b.   *non*polar covalent (two atoms of the same element)

    c.   polar covalent (different elements)

    d.   *non*polar covalent (atoms of the same element)

100.   In a diatomic molecule containing two different elements, the more electronegative atom will be the negative end of the molecule, and the *less* electronegative atom will be the positive end.

    a.   oxygen

    b.   bromine

    c.   iodine

102.   a.   Al $1s^2\,2s^2\,2p^6\,3s^2\,3p^1$

           Al^{3+} $1s^2\,2s^2\,2p^6$

           Ne has the same configuration as Al^{3+}.

    b.   Br $1s^2\,2s^2\,2p^6\,3s^2\,3p^6\,4s^2\,3d^{10}\,4p^5$

           Br^- $1s^2\,2s^2\,2p^6\,3s^2\,3p^6\,4s^2\,3d^{10}\,4p^6$

           Kr has the same configuration as Br^-.

    c.   Ca $1s^2\,2s^2\,2p^6\,3s^2\,3p^6\,4s^2$

           Ca^{2+} $1s^2\,2s^2\,2p^6\,3s^2\,3p^6$

           Ar has the same configuration as Ca^{2+}.

    d.   Li $1s^2\,2s^1$

           Li^+ $1s^2$

           He has the same configuration as Li^+.

    e.   F $1s^2\,2s^2\,2p^5$

           F^- $1s^2\,2s^2\,2p^6$

           Ne has the same configuration as F^-.

104.   a. Na_2Se: Na has one electron more than a noble gas; Se has two electrons fewer than a noble gas.

    b.   RbF: Rb has one electron more than a noble gas; F has one electron less than a noble gas.

    c. K_2Te: K has one electron more than a noble gas; Te has two electrons fewer than a noble gas.

    d.   BaSe: Ba has two electrons more than a noble gas; Se has two electrons fewer than a noble gas.

    e.   KAt: K has one electron more than a noble gas; At has one electron less than a noble gas.

    f.   FrCl: Fr has one electron more than a noble gas; Cl has one electron less than a noble gas.

106.   Relative ionic sizes are indicated in Figure 12.9.

     a. Na^+

     b. Al^{3+}

     c. F^-

     d. Na^+

108.   a.   H provides 1; N provides 5; each O provides 6; total valence electrons = 24

     b.   each H provides 1; S provides 6; each O provides 6; total valence electrons = 32

     c.   each H provides 1; P provides 5; each O provides 6; total valence electrons = 32

     d.   H provides 1; Cl provides 7; each O provides 6; total valence electrons = 32

110.   a. N_2H_4 : Each N provides 5 valence electrons. Each H provides 1 valence electron. Total valence electrons = 14

     b. C_2H_6 : Each C provides 4 valence electrons. Each H provides 1 valence electron. Total valence electrons = 14

     c. NCl_3 : N provides 5 valence electrons. Each Cl provides 7 valence electrons. Total valence electrons = 26

     d. $SiCl_4$: Si provides 4 valence electrons. Each Cl provides 7 valence electrons. Total valence electrons = 32

112.   a. NO_3^- : N provides 5 valence electrons. Each O provides 6 valence electrons. The 1– charge means one additional valence electron. Total valence electrons = 24

b. CO_3^{2-}: C provides 4 valence electrons. Each O provides 6 valence electrons. The 2– charge means two additional valence electrons. Total valence electrons = 24

$$\ddot{O}=C-\ddot{O}: \quad\longleftrightarrow\quad :\ddot{O}-C=\ddot{O} \quad\longleftrightarrow\quad :\ddot{O}-C-\ddot{O}:$$
$$\;\;\;\;| \qquad\qquad\qquad\; | \qquad\qquad\qquad\quad \|$$
$$\;\;\;:\ddot{O}: \qquad\qquad\qquad :\ddot{O}: \qquad\qquad\qquad\; :\ddot{O}:$$

c. NH_4^+: N provides 5 valence electrons. Each H provides 1 valence electron. The 1+ charge means one *less* valence electron. Total valence electrons = 8

$$\begin{array}{c} H \\ | \\ H-N-H \\ | \\ H \end{array}$$

114.   a.   four electron pairs arranged tetrahedrally about C

   b.   four electron pairs arranged tetrahedrally about Ge

   c.   three electron pairs arranged trigonally (planar) around B

116.   a. ClO_3^-, trigonal pyramid (lone pair on Cl)

   b. ClO_2^-, nonlinear (*V*-shaped, two lone pairs on Cl)

   c. ClO_4^-, tetrahedral (all pairs on Cl are bonding)

118.   a.   nonlinear (*V*–shaped)

   b.   trigonal planar

   c.   basically trigonal planar around the C (the H is attached to one of the O atoms, and distorts the shape around the carbon only slightly)

   d.   linear

120.   Ionic compounds tend to be hard, crystalline substances with relatively high melting and boiling points. Covalently bonded substances tend to be gases, liquids, or relatively soft solids, with much lower melting and boiling points.

CUMULATIVE REVIEW

Chapters 10–12

2. Temperature is a measure of the random motions of the components of a substance: in other words, temperature is a measure of the average kinetic energy of the particles in a sample. The molecules in warm water must be moving faster than the molecules in cold water (the molecules have the same mass, so if the temperature is higher, the average velocity of the particles must be higher in the warm water). Heat is the energy that flows because of a difference in temperature.

4. Thermodynamics is the study of energy and energy changes. The first law of thermodynamics is the law of conservation of energy: the energy of the universe is constant. Energy cannot be created or destroyed, only transferred from one place to another or from one form to another. The internal energy of a system, E, represents the total of the kinetic and potential energies of all the particles in a system. A flow of heat may be produced when there is a change in internal energy in the system, but it is not correct to say that the system "contains" the heat: part of the internal energy is *converted* to heat energy during the process (under other conditions, the change in internal energy might be expressed as work rather than a heat flow).

6. The enthalpy change represents the heat energy that flows (at constant pressure) on a molar basis when a reaction occurs. The enthalpy change is indeed a state function (which we make great use of in Hess's Law calculations). Enthalpy changes are typically measured in insulated reaction vessels called calorimeters (a simple calorimeter is shown in Figure 10.6 in the text).

8. Consider petroleum. A gallon of gasoline contains concentrated, stored energy. We can use that energy to make our car move, but when we do, the energy stored in the gasoline is dispersed to the environment. Although the energy is still there (it is conserved), it is no longer in a concentrated useful form. So although the energy content of the universe remains constant, the energy that is now stored in concentrated forms in oil, coal, wood, and other sources is gradually being dispersed to the universe where it can do no work.

10. A "driving force" is an effect that tends to make a process occur. Two important driving forces are dispersion of energy during a process or dispersion of matter during a process ("energy spread" and "matter spread"). For example, a log burns in a fireplace because the energy contained in the log is dispersed to the universe when it burns. If we put a teaspoon of sugar into a glass of water, the dissolving of the sugar is a favorable process because the matter of the sugar is dispersed when it dissolves. Entropy is a measure of the randomness or disorder in a system. The entropy of the universe is constant increasing because of "matter spread" and "energy spread". A spontaneous process is one that occurs without outside intervention: the spontaneity of a reaction depends on the energy spread and matter spread if the reaction takes place. A reaction that disperses energy and also disperses matter will always be spontaneous. Reactions that require an input of energy may still be spontaneous if the matter spread is large enough.

12. molar mass $CH_4 = 16.04$ g

    a. $0.521 \text{ mol} \times -\dfrac{890 \text{ kJ}}{1 \text{ mol}} = -464 \text{ kJ}$

    b. $1.25 \text{ g} \times \dfrac{1 \text{ mol}}{16.04 \text{ g}} \times \dfrac{-890 \text{ kJ}}{1 \text{ mol}} = -69.4 \text{ kJ}$

    c. $-1250 \text{ kJ} \times \dfrac{1 \text{ mol}}{-890 \text{ kJ}} = 1.40 \text{ mol} (22.5 \text{ g})$

14. An atom is said to be in its ground state when it is in its lowest possible energy state. When an atom possesses more energy than its ground state energy, the atom is said to be in an excited state. An atom is promoted from its ground state to an excited state by absorbing energy; when the atom returns from an excited state to its ground state it emits the excess energy as electromagnetic radiation. Atoms do not gain or emit radiation randomly, but rather do so only in discrete bundles of radiation called photons. The photons of radiation emitted by atoms are characterized by the wavelength (color) of the radiation: longer wavelength photons carry less energy than shorter wavelength photons. The energy of a photon emitted by an atom corresponds exactly to the difference in energy between two allowed energy states in an atom: thus, we can use an observable phenomenon (emission of light by excited atoms), to gain insight into the energy changes taking place within the atom.

16. Bohr pictured the electron moving in only certain circular orbits around the nucleus. Each particular orbit (corresponding to a particular distance from the nucleus) had associated with it a particular energy (resulting from the attraction between the nucleus and the electron). When an atom absorbs energy, the electron moves from its ground state in the orbit closest to the nucleus ($n = 1$) to an orbit farther away from the nucleus ($n = 2, 3, 4, ...$). When an excited atom returns to its ground state, corresponding to the electron moving from an outer orbit to the orbit nearest the nucleus, the atom emits the excess energy as radiation. As the Bohr orbits are of fixed distances from the nucleus and from each other, when an electron moves from one fixed orbit to another, the energy change is of a definite amount. This corresponds to a photon being emitted of a particular characteristic wavelength and energy. The original Bohr theory worked very well for hydrogen: Bohr even predicted emission wavelengths for hydrogen that had not yet been seen, but were subsequently found at the exact wavelengths Bohr had calculated. However, when the simple Bohr model for the atom was applied to the emission spectra of other elements, the theory could not predict or explain the observed emission spectra.

18. The lowest energy hydrogen atomic orbital is called the $1s$ orbital. The $1s$ orbital is spherical in shape (that is, the electron density around the nucleus is uniform in all directions from the nucleus). The $1s$ orbital represents a probability map of electron density around the nucleus for the first principal energy level. The orbital does not have a sharp edge (it appears fuzzy) because the probability of finding the electron does not drop off suddenly with distance from the nucleus. The orbital does not represent just a spherical surface on which the electron moves (this would be similar to Bohr's original theory). When we draw a picture to represent the $1s$ orbital we are indicating that the probability of finding the electron within this region of space is greater than 90%. We know that the likelihood of finding the electron within this orbital is very high, but we still don't know exactly where in this region the electron is at a given instant in time.

20.   The third principal energy level of hydrogen is divided into three sublevels, the 3*s*, 3*p*, and 3*d* sublevels. The 3*s* subshell consists of the single 3*s* orbital: like the other *s* orbitals, the 3*s* orbital is spherical in shape. The 3*p* subshell consists of a set of three equal-energy 3*p* orbitals: each of these 3*p* orbitals has the same shape ("dumbbell"), but each of the 3*p* orbitals is oriented in a different direction in space. The 3*d* subshell consists of a set of five 3*d* orbitals: the 3*d* orbitals have the shapes indicated in Figure 11.28, and are oriented in different directions around the nucleus (students sometimes say that the 3*d* orbitals have the shape of a 4-leaf clover). The fourth principal energy level of hydrogen is divided into four sublevels, the 4*s*, 4*p*, 4*d*, and 4*f* orbitals. The 4*s* subshell consists of the single 4*s* orbital. The 4*p* subshell consists of a set of three 4*p* orbitals. The 4*d* subshell consists of a set of five 4*d* orbitals. The shapes of the 4*s*, 4*p*, and 4*d* orbitals are the same as the shapes of the orbitals of the third principal energy level (the orbitals of the fourth principal energy level are larger and further from the nucleus than the orbitals of the third level, however). The fourth principal energy level, because it is further from the nucleus, also contains a 4*f* subshell, consisting of seven 4*f* orbitals (the shapes of the 4*f* orbitals are beyond the scope of this text).

22.   Atoms have a series of principal energy levels symbolized by the letter *n*. The *n* = 1 level is the closest to the nucleus, and the energies of the levels increase as the value of *n* increases going out from the nucleus. Each principal energy level is divided into a set of sublevels of different characteristic shapes (designated by the letters *s, p, d,* and *f*). Each sublevel is further subdivided into a set of orbitals: each *s* subshell consists of a single *s* orbital; each *p* subshell consists of a set of three *p* orbitals; each *d* subshell consists of a set of five *d* orbitals; etc. A given orbital can be empty or it can contain one or two electrons, but never more than two electrons (if an orbital contains two electrons, then the electrons must have opposite intrinsic spins). The shape we picture for an orbital represents only a probability map for finding electrons: the shape does not represent a trajectory or pathway for electron movements.

24.   The valence electrons are the electrons in an atom's outermost shell. The valence electrons are those most likely to be involved in chemical reactions because they are at the outside edge of the atom.

26.   From the column and row location of an element, you should be able to determine what the valence shell of an element has for its electronic configuration. For example, the element in the third horizontal row, in the second vertical column, has $3s^2$ as its valence configuration. We know that the valence electrons are in the *n* = 3 shell because the element is in the third horizontal row. We know that the valence electrons are *s* electrons because the first two electrons in a horizontal row are always in an *s* subshell. We know that there are two electrons because the element is the second element in the horizontal row. As an additional example, the element in the seventh vertical column of the second horizontal row in the periodic table has valence configuration $2s^22p^5$.

28.   The ionization energy of an atom represents the energy required to remove an electron from the atom. As one goes from top to bottom in a vertical group in the periodic table, the ionization energies decrease (it becomes easier to remove an electron). As one goes down within a group, the valence electrons are farther and farther from the nucleus and are less tightly held. The ionization energies increase when going from left to right within a horizontal row within the periodic table. The left-hand side of the periodic table is where the metallic elements are found, which lose electrons relatively easily. The right-hand side of the periodic table is where the nonmetallic elements are found: rather than losing electrons, these elements tend to gain electrons. Within a given horizontal row in the periodic table, the valence electrons are all in the

same principal energy shell: however, as you go from left to right in the horizontal row, the nuclear charge that holds onto the electrons is increasing one unit with each successive element, making it that much more difficult to remove an electron. The relative sizes of atoms also vary systematically with the location of an element in the periodic table. Within a given vertical group, the atoms get progressively larger when going from the top of the group to the bottom: the valence electrons of the atoms are in progressively higher principal energy shells (and are progressively further from the nucleus) as we go down in a group. In going from left to right within a horizontal row in the periodic table, the atoms get progressively smaller. Although all the elements in a given horizontal row in the periodic table have their valence electrons in the same principal energy shell, the nuclear charge is progressively increasing from left to right, making the given valence shell progressively smaller as the electrons are drawn more closely to the nucleus.

30.   Ionic bonding results when elements of very different electronegativities react with each other. Typically a metallic element reacts with a nonmetallic element; the metallic element losing electrons and forming positive ions and the nonmetallic element gaining electrons and forming negative ions. Sodium chloride, NaCl, is an example of a typical ionic compound. The aggregate form of such a compound consists of a crystal lattice of alternating positively and negatively charged ions. A given positive ion is attracted by several surrounding negatively charged ions, and a given negative ion is attracted by several surrounding positively charged ions. Similar electrostatic attractions go on in three dimensions throughout the crystal of ionic solid, leading to a very stable system (with very high melting and boiling points, for example). We know that ionic-bonded solids do not conduct electricity in the solid state (because the ions are held tightly in place by all the attractive forces), but such substances are strong electrolytes when melted or when dissolved in water (either process sets the ions free to move around).

32.   Electronegativity represents the relative ability of an atom in a molecule to attract shared electrons towards itself. In order for a bond to be polar, one of the atoms in the bond must attract the shared electron pair towards itself and away from the other atom of the bond: this can only happen if one atom of the bond is more electronegative than the other (that is, that there is a considerable difference in electronegativity for the two atoms of the bond). The larger the difference in electronegativity between two atoms joined in a bond, the more polar is the bond. Specific examples depend on student choice of elements, but in general, a molecule like Cl_2 would be non-polar because both atoms of the bond have the same electronegativity, whereas a molecule like HCl would be polar because there is an electronegativity difference between the two atoms in the bond.

34.   It has been observed over many experiments that when an active metal like sodium or magnesium reacts with a nonmetal, the sodium atoms always form Na^+ ions and the magnesium atoms always form Mg^{2+} ions. It has been further observed that aluminum always forms only the Al^{3+} ion. When nitrogen, oxygen, or fluorine form simple ions, the ions that are formed are always N^{3-}, O^{2-}, and F^-, respectively. Clearly the facts that these elements always form the same ions and that those ions all contain eight electrons in the outermost shell, led scientists to speculate that there must be something fundamentally stable about a species that has eight electrons in its outermost shell (like the noble gas neon). The repeated observation that so many elements, when reacting, tend to attain an electronic configuration that is isoelectronic with a noble gas led chemists to speculate that all elements try to attain such a configuration for their outermost shells. In general, when atoms of a metal react with atoms of a nonmetal, the metal atoms lose electrons until they have the configuration of the preceding noble gas, and the nonmetal atoms gain electrons until they have the configuration of the following noble gas. Covalently and polar covalently bonded molecules also strive to attain pseudo-noble gas electronic configurations. For a covalently

bonded molecule like F_2, in which neither fluorine atom has a greater tendency than the other to gain or lose electrons completely, each F atom provides one electron of the pair of electrons that constitutes the covalent bond. Each F atom feels also the influence of the other F atom's electron in the shared pair, and each F atom effectively fills its outermost shell. Similarly, in polar covalently bonded molecules like HF or HCl, the shared pair of electrons between the atoms effectively completes the outer electron shell of each atom simultaneously to give each atom a noble gas-like electronic configuration.

36.   Bonding between atoms to form a molecule involves only the valence electrons of the atoms (not the inner core electrons). So when we draw the Lewis structure of a molecule, we show only these valence electrons (both bonding valence electrons and nonbonding valence electrons, however). The most important requisite for the formation of a stable compound (which we try to demonstrate when we write Lewis structures) is that each atom of a molecule attains a noble gas electron configuration. When we write Lewis structures, we arrange the bonding and nonbonding valence electrons to try to complete the octet (or duet) for as many atoms as is possible.

38.   Obviously, you could choose practically any molecule for your discussion. Let's illustrate the method for ammonia, NH_3. First count up the total number of valence electrons available in the molecule (without regard to what atom they officially come from); remember that for the representative elements, the number of valence electrons is indicated by what group the element is found in on the periodic table. For NH_3, because nitrogen is in Group 5, one nitrogen atom would contribute five valence electrons. Because hydrogen atoms only have one electron each, the three hydrogen atoms provide an additional three valence electrons, for a total of eight valence electrons overall. Next write down the symbols for the atoms in the molecule, and use one pair of electrons (represented by a line) to form a bond between each pair of bound atoms.

$$\text{H}\!-\!\text{N}\!-\!\text{H}$$
$$|$$
$$\text{H}$$

These three bonds use six of the eight valence electrons. Since each hydrogen already has its duet in what we have drawn so far, while the nitrogen atom only has six electrons around it so far, the final two valence electrons must represent a lone pair on the nitrogen.

$$\overset{..}{\text{N}}$$
$$\text{H}\!-\!\text{N}\!-\!\text{H}$$
$$|$$
$$\text{H}$$

40.   There are several types of exceptions to the octet rule described in the text. The octet rule is really a "rule of thumb" which we apply to molecules unless we have some evidence that a molecule does not follow the rule. There are some common molecules that, from experimental measurements, we know do not follow the octet rule. Boron and beryllium compounds sometimes do not fit the octet rule. For example, in BF_3, the boron atom only has six valence electrons, whereas in BeF_2, the beryllium atom only has four valence electrons. Other molecules that are exceptions to the octet rule include any molecule with an odd number of valence electrons (such as NO or NO_2): you can't get an octet (an even number) of electrons around each atom in a molecule with an odd number of valence electrons. Even the oxygen gas we breathe is an exception to the octet rule: although we can write a Lewis structure for O_2 satisfying the octet rule for each oxygen, we know from experiment that O_2 contains unpaired electrons (which would not be consistent with a structure in which all the electrons were paired up.)

42.

Valence Pairs	Bond Angle	Example(s)
2	180°	BeF_2, BeH_2
3	120°	BCl_3
4	109.5°	CH_4, CCl_4, GeF_4

44. a. $[Kr]\, 5s^2$

b. $[Ne]\, 3s^2\, 3p^1$

c. $[Ne]\, 3s^2\, 3p^5$

d. $[Ar]\, 4s^1$

e. $[Ne]\, 3s^2\, 3p^4$

f. $[Ar]\, 4s^2\, 3d^{10}\, 4p^3$

46.

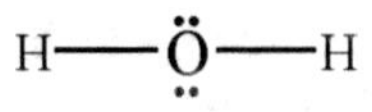 H—Ö—H	4 electron pairs tetrahedrally-oriented on O; non-linear (bent, *V*-shaped) geometry; H–O–H bond angle slightly less than 109.5° because of lone pairs.
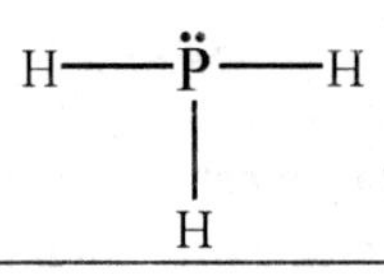 H—P̈—H (with H below)	4 electron pairs tetrahedrally-oriented on P; trigonal pyramidal geometry; H–P–H bond angles slightly less than 109.5° because of lone pair.
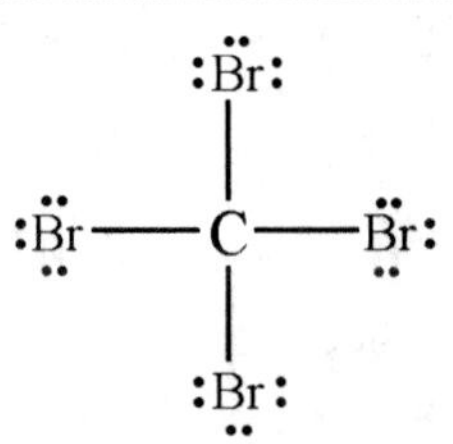 :Br: / :Br—C—Br: / :Br:	4 electron pairs tetrahedrally-oriented on C; overall tetrahedral geometry; Br–C–Br bond angles 109.5°
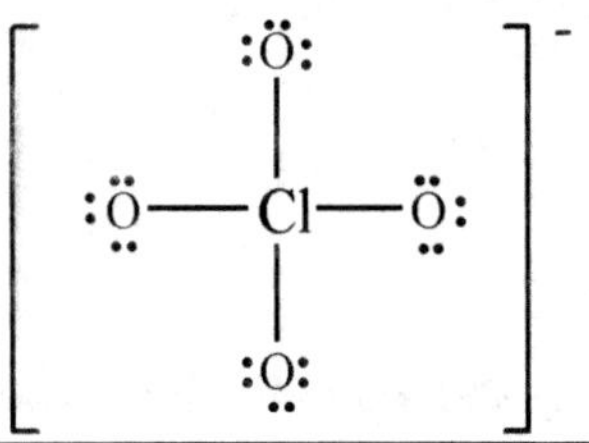 [:Ö: / :Ö—Cl—Ö: / :Ö:]⁻	4 electron pairs tetrahedrally-oriented on Cl; overall tetrahedral geometry; O–Cl–O bond angles 109.5°
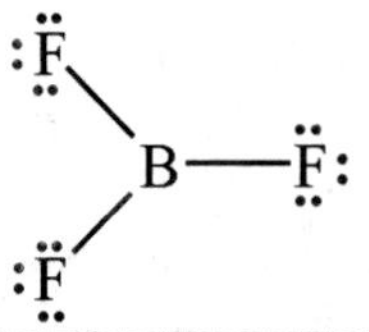 :F̈ / B—F̈: / :F̈	3 electron pairs trigonally-oriented on B (exception to octet rule); overall trigonal geometry; F–B–F bond angles 120°
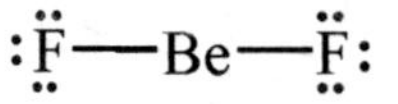 :F̈—Be—F̈:	2 electron pairs linearly-oriented on Be (exception to octet rule); overall linear geometry; F–Be–F bond angle 180°.

CHAPTER 13

Gases

2.   Solids and liquids have essentially fixed volumes and are not able to be compressed easily. Gases have volumes that depend on their conditions, and can be compressed or expanded by changes in those conditions. Although the particles of matter in solids are essentially fixed in position (the solid is rigid), the particles in liquids and gases are free to move.

4.   Figure 13.2 in the text shows a simple mercury barometer: a tube filled with mercury is inverted over a reservoir (containing mercury) that is open to the atmosphere. When the tube is inverted, the mercury falls to a level at which the pressure of the atmosphere is sufficient to support the column of mercury. One standard atmosphere of pressure is taken to be the pressure capable of supporting a column of mercury to a height of 760.0 mm above the reservoir level.

6.   Pressure units include mm Hg, torr, pascals, and psi. The unit "mm Hg" is derived from the barometer, since in a traditional mercury barometer, we measure the height of the mercury column (in millimeters) above the reservoir of mercury.

8.   1.00 atm = 760 torr = 760 mm Hg = 101.325 kPa = 14.70 psi

   a. $14.9 \text{ psi} \times \dfrac{1 \text{ atm}}{14.70 \text{ psi}} = 1.01 \text{ atm}$

   b. $795 \text{ torr} \times \dfrac{1 \text{ atm}}{760 \text{ torr}} = 1.05 \text{ atm}$

   c. $743 \text{ mm Hg} \times \dfrac{101.325 \text{ kPa}}{760 \text{ mm Hg}} = 99.1 \text{ kPa}$

   d. $99,436 \text{ Pa} \times \dfrac{1 \text{ kPa}}{1000 \text{ Pa}} = 99.436 \text{ kPa}$

10.   1.00 atm = 760 torr = 760 mm Hg = 101.325 kPa = 14.70 psi

   a. $17.3 \text{ psi} \times \dfrac{101.325 \text{ kPa}}{14.70 \text{ psi}} = 119 \text{ kPa}$

   b. $1.15 \text{ atm} \times \dfrac{14.70 \text{ psi}}{1 \text{ atm}} = 16.9 \text{ psi}$

   c. $4.25 \text{ atm} \times \dfrac{760 \text{ mm Hg}}{1 \text{ atm}} = 3.23 \times 10^3 \text{ mm Hg}$

   d. $224 \text{ psi} \times \dfrac{1 \text{ atm}}{14.70 \text{ psi}} = 15.2 \text{ atm}$

12. $1.00 \text{ atm} = 760 \text{ torr} = 760 \text{ mm Hg} = 101.325 \text{ kPa} = 14.70 \text{ psi}$

    a. $6.42 \text{ atm} \times \dfrac{101.325 \text{ kPa}}{1 \text{ atm}} = 651 \text{ kPa}$

    b. $4.21 \text{ atm} \times \dfrac{760 \text{ torr}}{1 \text{ atm}} = 3.20 \times 10^3 \text{ torr}$

    c. $794 \text{ mm Hg} \times \dfrac{1 \text{ atm}}{760 \text{ mm Hg}} = 1.04 \text{ atm}$

    d. $27.2 \text{ psi} \times \dfrac{1 \text{ atm}}{14.70 \text{ psi}} = 1.85 \text{ atm}$

14. Additional mercury increases the pressure on the gas sample, causing the volume of the gas upon which the pressure is exerted to decrease (Boyle's Law)

16. $PV = k; \quad P_1V_1 = P_2V_2$

18.   a. $P_1 = 1.15 \text{ atm}$ $P_2 = 775 \text{ mm Hg} = 1.020 \text{ atm}$

       $V_1 = 375 \text{ mL}$ $V_2 = ?$

       $V_2 = \dfrac{P_1V_1}{P_2} = \dfrac{(1.15 \text{ atm})(375 \text{ mL})}{(1.020 \text{ atm})} = 423 \text{ mL}$

  b. $P_1 = 1.08 \text{ atm}$ $P_2 = 135 \text{ kPa} = 1.33 \text{ atm}$

       $V_1 = 195 \text{ mL}$ $V_2 = ?$

       $V_2 = \dfrac{P_1V_1}{P_2} = \dfrac{(1.08 \text{ atm})(195 \text{ mL})}{(1.33 \text{ atm})} = 158 \text{ mL}$

  c. $P_1 = 131 \text{ kPa} = 982.6 \text{ mm Hg}$ $P_2 = 765 \text{ mm Hg}$

       $V_1 = 6.75 \text{ L}$ $V_2 = ?$

       $V_2 = \dfrac{P_1V_1}{P_2} = \dfrac{(982.6 \text{ mm Hg})(6.75 \text{ L})}{(765 \text{ mm Hg})} = 8.67 \text{ L}$

20.   a. $P_1 = 755 \text{ mm Hg}$ $P_2 = ?$

       $V_1 = 125 \text{ mL}$ $V_2 = 137 \text{ mL}$

       $P_2 = \dfrac{P_1V_1}{V_2} = \dfrac{(755 \text{ mm Hg})(125 \text{ mL})}{(137 \text{ mL})} = 689 \text{ mm Hg}$

  b. $P_1 = 1.08 \text{ atm}$ $P_2 = ?$

       $V_1 = 331 \text{ mL}$ $V_2 = 299 \text{ mL}$

       $P_2 = \dfrac{P_1V_1}{V_2} = \dfrac{(1.08 \text{ atm})(331 \text{ mL})}{(299 \text{ mL})} = 1.20 \text{ atm}$

c. $P_1 = 789$ mm Hg $P_2 = 135$ kPa $= 1013$ mm Hg

        $V_1 = 3.02$ L $V_2 = ?$

$$V_2 = \frac{P_1V_1}{P_2} = \frac{(789 \text{ mm Hg})(3.02 \text{ L})}{(1013 \text{ mm Hg})} = 2.35 \text{ L}$$

22. $P_1 = P_1$ $P_2 = 2 \times P_1$

       $V_1 = 1.04$ L $V_2 = ?$ L

$$V_2 = \frac{P_1V_1}{P_2} = \frac{(P_1)(1.04 \text{ L})}{(2 \times P_1)} = \frac{1.04 \text{ L}}{2} = 0.520 \text{ L}$$

24. $P_2 = \dfrac{P_1V_1}{V_2} = \dfrac{(1.00 \text{ atm})(27.2 \text{ mL})}{(1.00 \text{ mL})} = 27.2 \text{ atm}$

26.   Charles's Law indicates that an ideal gas decreases by 1/273 of its volume for every degree Celsius its temperature is lowered. This means an ideal gas would approach a volume of zero at – 273°C.

28. $V = kT$; $V_1/T_1 = V_2/T_2$

30. $V_1 = 375$ mL $V_2 = ?$ mL

       $T_1 = 78°C = 351$ K $T_2 = 22°C = 295$ K

$$V_2 = \frac{V_1T_2}{T_1} = \frac{(375 \text{ mL})(295 \text{ K})}{(351 \text{ K})} = 315 \text{ mL}$$

32.   a. $V_1 = 73.5$ mL $V_2 = ?$ L

             $T_1 = 0°C = 273$ K $T_2 = 25°C = 298$ K

$$V_2 = \frac{V_1T_2}{T_1} = \frac{(73.5 \text{ mL})(298 \text{ K})}{(273 \text{ K})} = 80.2 \text{ mL}$$

      b. $V_1 = 15.2$ L $V_2 = 10.0$ L

             $T_1 = 25°C = 298$ K $T_2 = ?°C$

$$T_2 = \frac{V_2T_1}{V_1} = \frac{(10.0 \text{ L})(298 \text{ K})}{(15.2 \text{ L})} = 196 \text{ K} = -77°C$$

      c. $V_1 = 1.75$ mL $V_2 = ?$ mL

             $T_1 = 2.3$ K $T_2 = 0°C = 273$ K

$$V_2 = \frac{V_1T_2}{T_1} = \frac{(1.75 \text{ mL})(273 \text{ K})}{(2.3 \text{ K})} = 208 \text{ mL} \ (2.1 \times 10^2 \text{ mL})$$

34.   a. $V_1 = 2.01 \times 10^2$ L $V_2 = 5.00$ L

               $T_1 = 1150°C = 1423$ K $T_2 = ?°C$

$$T_2 = \frac{V_2 T_1}{V_1} = \frac{(5.00 \text{ L})(1423 \text{ K})}{(201 \text{ L})} = 35.4 \text{ K} = -238°C$$

     b. $V_1 = 44.2$ mL $V_2 = ?$ mL

               $T_1 = 298$ K $T_2 = 0$

$$V_2 = \frac{V_1 T_2}{T_1} = \frac{(44.2 \text{ mL})(0 \text{ K})}{(298 \text{ K})} = 0 \text{ mL} \text{ (0 K is absolute zero)}$$

     c. $V_1 = 44.2$ mL $V_2 = ?$ mL

               $T_1 = 298$ K $T_2 = 0°C = 273$ K

$$V_2 = \frac{V_1 T_2}{T_1} = \frac{(44.2 \text{ mL})(273 \text{ K})}{(298 \text{ K})} = 40.5 \text{ mL}$$

36. $V_2 = \dfrac{V_1 T_2}{T_1} = \dfrac{(125 \text{ mL})(250 \text{ K})}{(450 \text{ K})} = 69.4 \text{ mL} = 69 \text{ mL to two significant figures}$

38. $V_2 = \dfrac{V_1 T_2}{T_1}$

Temp, °C	90	80	70	60	50	40	30	20
Volume, mL	124	121	117	113	110	107	103	100

40. $V = an$; $V_1/n_1 = V_2/n_2$

42. $V = an$; $V_1/n_1 = V_2/n_2$

     Since 2.08 g of chlorine contains twice the number of moles of gas contained in the 1.04 g sample, the volume of the 2.08 g sample will be twice as large = 1744 (1.74×10^3) mL

44.   molar mass of Ar = 39.95 g

$$2.71 \text{ g Ar} \times \frac{1 \text{ mol}}{39.95 \text{ g}} = 0.0678 \text{ mol Ar}$$

$$4.21 \text{ L} \times \frac{1.29 \text{ mol}}{0.0678 \text{ mol}} = 80.1 \text{ L}$$

46.   Real gases most closely approach ideal gas behavior under conditions of relatively high temperatures (0°C or higher) and relatively low pressures (1 atm or lower).

48.   For an ideal gas, $PV = nRT$ is true under any conditions. Consider a particular sample of gas (so that n remains constant) at a particular fixed pressure (so that P remains constant also). Suppose that at temperature T_1 the volume of the gas sample is V_1. Then for this set of conditions, the ideal gas equation would be given by

$PV_1 = nRT_1.$

If we then change the temperature of the gas sample to a new temperature T_2, the volume of the gas sample changes to a new volume V_2. For this new set of conditions, the ideal gas equation would be given by

$PV_2 = nRT_2.$

If we make a ratio of these two expressions for the ideal gas equation for this gas sample, and cancel out terms that are constant for this situation (P, n, and R) we get

$$\frac{PV_1}{PV_2} = \frac{nRT_1}{nRT_2}$$

$$\frac{V_1}{V_2} = \frac{T_1}{T_2}$$

This can be rearranged to the familiar form of Charles's law

$$\frac{V_1}{T_1} = \frac{V_2}{T_2}$$

50.   a. $P = 782$ mm Hg $= 1.03$ atm; $T = 27°C = 300$ K

$$V = \frac{nRT}{P} = \frac{(0.210 \text{ mol})(0.08206 \text{ L atm mol}^{-1} \text{ K}^{-1})(300 \text{ K})}{(1.03 \text{ atm})} = 5.02 \text{ L}$$

b. $V = 644$ mL $= 0.644$ L

$$P = \frac{nRT}{V} = \frac{(0.0921 \text{ mol})(0.08206 \text{ L atm mol}^{-1} \text{ K}^{-1})(303 \text{ K})}{(0.644 \text{ L})} = 3.56 \text{ atm}$$

$$= 2.70 \times 10^3 \text{ mm Hg}$$

c. $P = 745$ mm $= 0.980$ atm

$$T = \frac{PV}{nR} = \frac{(0.980 \text{ atm})(11.2 \text{ L})}{(0.401 \text{ mol})(0.08206 \text{ L atm mol}^{-1} \text{ K}^{-1})} = 334 \text{ K}$$

52.   molar mass Ar $= 39.95$ g; $25°C = 298$ K

$$12.2 \text{ g Ar} \times \frac{1 \text{ mol Ar}}{39.95 \text{ g Ar}} = 0.3054 \text{ mol Ar}$$

$$P = \frac{nRT}{V} = \frac{(0.3054 \text{ mol})(0.08206 \text{ L atm mol}^{-1} \text{ K}^{-1})(298 \text{ K})}{(10.0 \text{ L})} = 0.747 \text{ atm}$$

54.   molar mass Ar $= 39.95$ g; 40.0 g $= 1.001$ mol

$$T = \frac{PV}{nR} = \frac{(1.00 \text{ atm})(25.00 \text{ L})}{(1.001 \text{ mol})(0.08206 \text{ L atm mol}^{-1} \text{ K}^{-1})} = 304 \text{ K} = 31°C$$

56.   molar mass Ne = 20.18 g; 25°C = 298 K; 50°C = 323 K

$$1.25 \text{ g Ne} \times \frac{1 \text{ mol}}{20.18 \text{ g}} = 0.06194 \text{ mol}$$

$$P = \frac{nRT}{V} = \frac{(0.06194 \text{ mol})(0.08206 \text{ L atm mol}^{-1} \text{ K}^{-1})(298 \text{ K})}{(10.1 \text{ L})} = 0.150 \text{ atm}$$

$$P = \frac{nRT}{V} = \frac{(0.06194 \text{ mol})(0.08206 \text{ L atm mol}^{-1} \text{ K}^{-1})(323 \text{ K})}{(10.1 \text{ L})} = 0.163 \text{ atm}$$

58.   molar mass O_2 = 32.00 g; 784 mm Hg = 1.032 atm

$$4.25 \text{ g } O_2 \times \frac{1 \text{ mol } O_2}{32.00 \text{ g } O_2} = 0.1328 \text{ mol}$$

$$T = \frac{PV}{nR} = \frac{(1.032 \text{ atm})(2.51 \text{ L})}{(0.1328 \text{ mol})(0.08206 \text{ L atm mol}^{-1} \text{ K}^{-1})} = 238 \text{ K} = -35°C$$

60.   Molar masses: He, 4.003 g; Ar, 39.95 g

$$4.15 \text{ g He} \times \frac{1 \text{ mol He}}{4.003 \text{ g He}} = 1.037 \text{ mol He}$$

$$56.2 \text{ g Ar} \times \frac{1 \text{ mol Ar}}{39.95 \text{ g Ar}} = 1.407 \text{ mol Ar}$$

$$\text{For He, } P = \frac{nRT}{V} = \frac{(1.037 \text{ mol})(0.08206 \text{ L atm mol}^{-1} \text{ K}^{-1})(298 \text{ K})}{(5.00 \text{ L})} = 5.07 \text{ atm}$$

$$\text{For Ar, } P = \frac{nRT}{V} = \frac{(1.407 \text{ mol})(0.08206 \text{ L atm mol}^{-1} \text{ K}^{-1})(303 \text{ K})}{(10.00 \text{ L})} = 3.50 \text{ atm}$$

The helium is at a higher pressure than the argon.

62.   molar mass Ar = 39.95 g; 29°C = 302 K; 42°C = 315 K

$$1.29 \text{ g Ar} \times \frac{1 \text{ mol Ar}}{39.95 \text{ g Ar}} = 0.03329 \text{ mol Ar}$$

$$P = \frac{nRT}{V} = \frac{(0.03329 \text{ mol})(0.08206 \text{ L atm mol}^{-1} \text{ K}^{-1})(302 \text{ K})}{(2.41 \text{ L})} = 0.332 \text{ atm}$$

$$P = \frac{nRT}{V} = \frac{(0.03329 \text{ mol})(0.08206 \text{ L atm mol}^{-1} \text{ K}^{-1})(315 \text{ K})}{(2.41 \text{ L})} = 0.346 \text{ atm}$$

64.   Molar mass of H_2O = 18.02 g; 2.0 mL = 0.0020 L; 225°C = 498 K

$$0.250 \text{ g } H_2O \times \frac{1 \text{ mol } H_2O}{18.02 \text{ g } H_2O} = 0.01387 \text{ mol } H_2O$$

$$P = \frac{nRT}{V} = \frac{(0.01387 \text{ mol})(0.08206 \text{ L atm mol}^{-1} \text{ K}^{-1})(498 \text{ K})}{(0.0020 \text{ L})} = 283 \text{ atm} = 2.8 \times 10^2 \text{ atm}$$

66.   As a gas is bubbled through water, the bubbles of gas become saturated with water vapor, thus forming a gaseous mixture. The total pressure in a sample of gas that has been collected by bubbling through water is made up of two components: the pressure of the gas of interest and the pressure of water vapor. The partial pressure of the gas of interest is then the total pressure of the sample minus the vapor pressure of water.

68.   molar masses: Ne, 20.18 g; Ar, 39.95 g; 27°C = 300 K

$$1.28 \text{ g Ne} \times \frac{1 \text{ mol Ne}}{20.18 \text{ g Ne}} = 0.06343 \text{ mol Ne}$$

$$2.49 \text{ g Ar} \times \frac{1 \text{ mol Ar}}{39.95 \text{ g Ar}} = 0.06233 \text{ mol Ar}$$

$$P_{\text{neon}} = \frac{n_{neon}RT}{V} = \frac{(0.06343 \text{ mol})(0.08206 \text{ L atm mol}^{-1} \text{ K}^{-1})(300 \text{ K})}{(9.87 \text{ L})} = 0.1582 \text{ atm}$$

$$P_{\text{argon}} = \frac{n_{argon}RT}{V} = \frac{(0.06233 \text{ mol})(0.08206 \text{ L atm mol}^{-1} \text{ K}^{-1})(300 \text{ K})}{(9.87 \text{ L})} = 0.1555 \text{ atm}$$

P_{total} = 0.1582 atm + 0.1555 atm = 0.314 atm

70.   925 mm Hg = 1.217 atm; 26°C = 299 K; molar masses: Ne, 20.18 g; Ar, 39.95 g

$$n = \frac{PV}{RT} = \frac{(1.217 \text{ atm})(3.00 \text{ L})}{(0.08206 \text{ L atm mol}^{-1} \text{ K}^{-1})(299 \text{ K})} = 0.1488 \text{ mol}$$

The number of moles of an ideal gas required to fill a given-sized container to a particular pressure at a particular temperature does not depend on the specific identity of the gas. So 0.1488 mol of Ne gas or 0.1488 mol of Ar gas would give the same pressure in the same flask at the same temperature.

$$\text{mass Ne} = 0.1488 \text{ mol Ne} \times \frac{20.18 \text{ g Ne}}{1 \text{ mol Ne}} = 3.00 \text{ g Ne}$$

$$\text{mass Ar} = 0.1488 \text{ mol Ar} \times \frac{39.95 \text{ g Ar}}{1 \text{ mol Ar}} = 5.94 \text{ g Ar}$$

72.   molar masses: He, 4.003 g; Ar, 39.95 g; 273°C = 546 K

$$1.15 \text{ g He} \times \frac{1 \text{ mol He}}{4.003 \text{ g Ne}} = 0.2873 \text{ mol He}$$

$$2.91 \text{ g Ar} \times \frac{1 \text{ mol Ar}}{39.95 \text{ g Ar}} = 0.07284 \text{ mol Ar}$$

$$P_{helium} = \frac{n_{helium}RT}{V} = \frac{(0.2873 \text{ mol})(0.08206 \text{ L atm mol}^{-1} \text{ K}^{-1})(546 \text{ K})}{(5.25 \text{ L})} = 2.452 \text{ atm}$$

$$P_{argon} = \frac{n_{argon}RT}{V} = \frac{(0.07284 \text{ mol})(0.08206 \text{ L atm mol}^{-1} \text{ K}^{-1})(546 \text{ K})}{(5.25 \text{ L})} = 0.6216 \text{ atm}$$

$P_{total} = 0.1582 \text{ atm} + 0.1555 \text{ atm} = 3.07 \text{ atm}$

74. $1.032 \text{ atm} = 784.3 \text{ mm Hg}$; molar mass of Zn = 65.38 g

$P_{hydrogen} = 784.3 \text{ mm Hg} - 32 \text{ mm Hg} = 752.3 \text{ mm Hg} = 0.990 \text{ atm}$

$V = 240 \text{ mL} = 0.240 \text{ L}$; $T = 30°C + 273 = 303 \text{ K}$

$$n_{hydrogen} = \frac{PV}{RT} = \frac{(0.990 \text{ atm})(0.240 \text{ L})}{(0.08206 \text{ L atm mol}^{-1} \text{ K}^{-1})(303 \text{ K})} = 0.00956 \text{ mol hydrogen}$$

$$0.00956 \text{ mol H}_2 \times \frac{1 \text{ mol Zn}}{1 \text{ mol H}_2} = 0.00956 \text{ mol of Zn must have reacted}$$

$$0.00956 \text{ mol Zn} \times \frac{65.38 \text{ g Zn}}{1 \text{ mol Zn}} = 0.625 \text{ g Zn must have reacted}$$

76. A theory is successful if it explains known experimental observations. Theories that have been successful in the past may not be successful in the future (for example, as technology evolves, more sophisticated experiments may be possible in the future).

78. pressure

80. no

82. If the temperature of a sample of gas is increased, the average kinetic energy of the particles of gas increases. This means that the speeds of the particles increase. If the particles have a higher speed, they will hit the walls of the container more frequently and with greater force, thereby increasing the pressure.

84. Standard Temperature and Pressure, STP = 0°C, 1 atm pressure. These conditions were chosen because they are easy to attain and reproduce *experimentally*. The barometric pressure within a laboratory is likely to be near 1 atm most days, and 0°C can be attained with a simple ice bath.

86. Molar mass of C = 12.01 g; 25°C = 298 K

$$1.25 \text{ g C} \times \frac{1 \text{ mol}}{12.01 \text{ g}} = 0.1041 \text{ mol C}$$

Since the balanced chemical equation shows a 1:1 stoichiometric relationship between C and O_2, then 0.1041 mol of O_2 will be needed

$$V = \frac{nRT}{P} = \frac{(0.1041 \text{ mol})(0.08206 \text{ L atm mol}^{-1} \text{ K}^{-1})(298 \text{ K})}{(1.02 \text{ atm})} = 2.50 \text{ L O}_2$$

88.   Molar mass of Mg = 24.31 g; STP: 1.00 atm, 273 K

$$1.02 \text{ g Mg} \times \frac{1 \text{ mol}}{24.31 \text{ g}} = 0.0420 \text{ mol Mg}$$

As the coefficients for Mg and Cl_2 in the balanced equation are the same, for 0.0420 mol of Mg reacting we will need 0.0420 mol of Cl_2.

$$V = 0.0420 \text{ mol Cl}_2 \times \frac{22.4 \text{ L}}{1 \text{ mol}} = 0.941 \text{ L Cl}_2 \text{ at STP.}$$

90.   molar mass CaC_2 = 64.10 g; 25°C = 298 K

$$2.49 \text{ g CaC}_2 \times \frac{1 \text{ mol}}{64.10 \text{ g}} = 0.03885 \text{ mol CaC}_2$$

From the balanced chemical equation for the reaction, 0.03885 mol of CaC_2 reacting completely would generate 0.03885 mol of acetylene, C_2H_2

$$V = \frac{nRT}{P} = \frac{(0.03885 \text{ mol})(0.08206 \text{ L atm mol}^{-1} \text{ K}^{-1})(298 \text{ K})}{(1.01 \text{ atm})} = 0.941 \text{ L}$$

$$V = \frac{nRT}{P} = \frac{(0.03885 \text{ mol})(0.08206 \text{ L atm mol}^{-1} \text{ K}^{-1})(273 \text{ K})}{(1.00 \text{ atm})} = 0.870 \text{ L at STP}$$

92.   Molar mass of Mg_3N_2 = 100.95 g; T = 24°C = 297 K; P = 752 mm Hg = 0.989 atm

$$10.3 \text{ g Mg}_3\text{N}_2 \times \frac{1 \text{ mol}}{100.95 \text{ g}} = 0.102 \text{ mol Mg}_3\text{N}_2$$

From the balanced chemical equation, the amount of NH_3 produced will be

$$0.102 \text{ mol Mg}_3\text{N}_2 \times \frac{2 \text{ mol NH}_3}{1 \text{ mol Mg}_3\text{N}_2} = 0.204 \text{ mol NH}_3$$

$$V = \frac{nRT}{P} = \frac{(0.204 \text{ mol})(0.08206 \text{ L atm mol}^{-1} \text{ K}^{-1})(297 \text{ K})}{(0.989 \text{ atm})} = 5.03 \text{ L}$$

This assumes that the ammonia was collected dry.

94.   Molar masses: O_2, 32.00 g; N_2, 28.02 g; T = 35°C = 308 K; P = 755 mm Hg = 0.993 atm

$$26.2 \text{ g O}_2 \times \frac{1 \text{ mol O}_2}{32.00 \text{ g O}_2} = 0.819 \text{ mol O}_2$$

$$35.1 \text{ g N}_2 \times \frac{1 \text{ mol N}_2}{28.02 \text{ g N}_2} = 1.25 \text{ mol N}_2$$

total moles = 0.819 mol + 1.25 mol = 2.07 mol

$$V = \frac{nRT}{P} = \frac{(2.07 \text{ mol})(0.08206 \text{ L atm mol}^{-1} \text{ K}^{-1})(308 \text{ K})}{(0.993 \text{ atm})} = 52.7 \text{ L}$$

96.   molar masses: He, 4.003 g; Ar, 39.95 g

$$5.02 \text{ g He} \times \frac{1 \text{ mol He}}{4.003 \text{ g He}} = 1.254 \text{ mol He}$$

$$1.254 \text{ mol He} \times \frac{22.4 \text{ L}}{1 \text{ mol}} = 28.1 \text{ L}$$

$$42.1 \text{ g Ar} \times \frac{1 \text{ mol Ar}}{39.95 \text{ g Ar}} = 1.054 \text{ mol Ar}$$

$$1.054 \text{ mol Ar} \times \frac{22.4 \text{ L}}{1 \text{ mol}} = 23.6 \text{ L}$$

98.   Molar masses: He, 4.003 g; Ne, 20.18 g

$$6.25 \text{ g He} \times \frac{1 \text{ mol He}}{4.003 \text{ g He}} = 1.561 \text{ mol He}$$

$$4.97 \text{ g Ne} \times \frac{1 \text{ mol Ne}}{20.18 \text{ g Ne}} = 0.2463 \text{ mol Ne}$$

n_{total} = 1.561 mol + 0.2463 mol = 1.807 mol

As 1 mol of an ideal gas occupies 22.4 L at STP, the volume is given by

$$1.807 \text{ mol} \times \frac{22.4 \text{ L}}{1 \text{ mol}} = 40.48 \text{ L} = 40.5 \text{ L}.$$

The partial pressure of a given gas in a mixture will be proportional to what *fraction* of the total number of moles of gas the given gas represents

$$P_{\text{He}} = \frac{1.561 \text{ mol He}}{1.807 \text{ mol total}} \times 1.00 \text{ atm} = 0.8639 \text{ atm} = 0.864 \text{ atm}$$

$$P_{\text{Ne}} = \frac{0.2463 \text{ mol Ne}}{1.807 \text{ mol total}} \times 1.00 \text{ atm} = 0.1363 \text{ atm} = 0.136 \text{ atm}$$

100. $2C_2H_2(g) + 5O_2(g) \rightarrow 2H_2O(g) + 4CO_2(g)$

molar mass C_2H_2 = 26.04 g

$$1.00 \text{ g C}_2\text{H}_2 \times \frac{1 \text{ mol}}{26.04 \text{ g}} = 0.0384 \text{ mol C}_2\text{H}_2$$

From the balanced chemical equation, $2 \times 0.0384 = 0.0768$ mol of CO_2 will be produced.

$$0.0768 \text{ mol } CO_2 \times \frac{22.4 \text{ L}}{1 \text{ mol}} = 1.72 \text{ L at STP}$$

102. 125 mL = 0.125 L

$$0.125 \text{ L} \times \frac{1 \text{ mol}}{22.4 \text{ L}} = 0.00558 \text{ mol } H_2$$

From the balanced chemical equation, one mole of zinc is required for each mole of hydrogen produced. Therefore, 0.00558 mol of Zn will be required.

$$0.00558 \text{ mol } Zn \times \frac{65.38 \text{ g } Zn}{1 \text{ mol}} = 0.365 \text{ g } Zn$$

104. twice

106. a. $PV = k;\ P_1V_1 = P_2V_2$

b. $V = kT;\ V_1/T_1 = V_2/T_2$

c. $V = an;\ V_1/n_1 = V_2/n_2$

d. $PV = nRT$

e. $P_1V_1/T_1 = P_2V_2/T_2$

108. First determine what volume the helium in the tank would have if it were at a pressure of 755 mm Hg (corresponding to the pressure the gas will have in the balloons).

8.40 atm = 6384 mm Hg

$$V_2 = (25.2 \text{ L}) \times \frac{6384 \text{ mm Hg}}{755 \text{ mm Hg}} = 213 \text{ L}$$

Allowing for the fact that 25.2 L of He will have to remain in the tank, this leaves 213 – 25.2 = 187.8 L of He for filling the balloons.

$$187.8 \text{ L He} \times \frac{1 \text{ balloon}}{1.50 \text{ L He}} = 125 \text{ balloons}$$

110. According to the balanced chemical equation, when 1 mol of $(NH_4)_2CO_3$ reacts, a total of 4 moles of gaseous substances is produced.

molar mass $(NH_4)_2CO_3$ = 96.09 g; 453 °C = 726 K

$$52.0 \text{ g} \times \frac{1 \text{ mol}}{96.09 \text{ g}} = 0.541 \text{ mol}$$

As 0.541 mol of $(NH_4)_2CO_3$ reacts, 4(0.541) = 2.16 mol of gaseous products result.

$$V = \frac{nRT}{P} = \frac{(2.16 \text{ mol})(0.08206 \text{ L atm mol}^{-1} \text{ K}^{-1})(726 \text{ K})}{(1.04 \text{ atm})} = 124 \text{ L}$$

112. $CaCO_3(s) + 2H^+(aq) \rightarrow Ca^{2+}(aq) + H_2O(l) + CO_2(g)$

molar mass $CaCO_3$ = 100.1 g; 60°C + 273 = 333 K

$$10.0 \text{ g } CaCO_3 \times \frac{1 \text{ mol}}{100.1 \text{ g}} = 0.0999 \text{ mol } CaCO_3 = 0.0999 \text{ mol } CO_2 \text{ also}$$

$P_{carbon\ dioxide} = P_{total} - P_{water\ vapor}$

$P_{carbon\ dioxide}$ = 774 mm Hg – 149.4 mm Hg = 624.6 mm Hg = 0.822 atm

$$V_{wet} = \frac{nRT}{P} = \frac{(0.0999 \text{ mol})(0.08206 \text{ L atm mol}^{-1} \text{ K}^{-1})(333 \text{ K})}{(0.822 \text{ atm})} = 3.32 \text{ L wet } CO_2$$

$$V_{dry} = 3.32 \text{ L} \times \frac{624.6 \text{ mm Hg}}{774 \text{ mm Hg}} = 2.68 \text{ L}$$

114. $2KClO_3(s) \rightarrow 2KCl(s) + 3O_2(g)$

molar mass $KClO_3$ = 122.6 g; 25°C + 273 = 298 K; 630. torr = 0.829 atm

$$50.0 \text{ g } KClO_3 \times \frac{1 \text{ mol } KClO_3}{122.6 \text{ g } KClO_3} = 0.408 \text{ mol } KClO_3$$

$$0.408 \text{ mol } KClO_3 \times \frac{3 \text{ mol } O_2}{2 \text{ mol } KClO_3} = 0.612 \text{ mol } O_2$$

$$V = \frac{nRT}{P} = \frac{(0.612 \text{ mol})(0.08206 \text{ L atm mol}^{-1} \text{ K}^{-1})(298 \text{ K})}{(0.829 \text{ atm})} = 18.1 \text{ L } O_2$$

116.   a. $752 \text{ mm Hg} \times \dfrac{101,325 \text{ Pa}}{760 \text{ mm Hg}} = 1.00 \times 10^5 \text{ Pa}$

   b. $458 \text{ kPa} \times \dfrac{1 \text{ atm}}{101.325 \text{ kPa}} = 4.52 \text{ atm}$

   c. $1.43 \text{ atm} \times \dfrac{760 \text{ mm Hg}}{1 \text{ atm}} = 1.09 \times 10^3 \text{ mm Hg}$

   d.   842 torr = 842 mm Hg

118.   a. $645 \text{ mm Hg} \times \dfrac{101,325 \text{ Pa}}{760 \text{ mm Hg}} = 8.60 \times 10^4 \text{ Pa}$

   b. $221 \text{ kPa} = 221 \times 10^3 \text{ Pa} = 2.21 \times 10^5 \text{ Pa}$

   c. $0.876 \text{ atm} \times \dfrac{101,325 \text{ Pa}}{1 \text{ atm}} = 8.88 \times 10^4 \text{ Pa}$

   d. $32 \text{ torr} \times \dfrac{101,325 \text{ Pa}}{760 \text{ torr}} = 4.3 \times 10^3 \text{ Pa}$

120.   a.   1.00 mm Hg = 1.00 torr

$$V = 255 \text{ mL} \times \frac{1.00 \text{ torr}}{2.00 \text{ torr}} = 128 \text{ mL}$$

      b.   1.0 atm = 101.325 kPa

$$V = 1.3 \text{ L} \times \frac{1.0 \text{ kPa}}{101.325 \text{ kPa}} = 1.3 \times 10^{-2} \text{ L}$$

      c.   1.0 mm Hg = 0.133 kPa

$$V = 1.3 \text{ L} \times \frac{1.0 \text{ kPa}}{0.133 \text{ kPa}} = 9.8 \text{ L}$$

122. $1.52 \text{ L} = 1.52 \times 10^3 \text{ mL}$

$$755 \text{ mm Hg} \times \frac{1.52 \times 10^3 \text{ mL}}{450 \text{ mL}} = 2.55 \times 10^3 \text{ mm Hg}$$

124.   a.   74°C + 273 = 347 K; −74°C + 273 = 199 K

$$100. \text{ mL} \times \frac{199 \text{ K}}{347 \text{ K}} = 57.3 \text{ mL}$$

      b.   100°C + 273 = 373 K

$$373 \text{ K} \times \frac{600 \text{ mL}}{500 \text{ mL}} = 448 \text{ K } (175°C)$$

      c.   zero (the volume of any gas sample becomes zero at 0 K)

126.   12°C + 273 = 285 K; 192°C + 273 = 465 K

$$75.2 \text{ mL} \times \frac{465 \text{ K}}{285 \text{ K}} = 123 \text{ mL}$$

128.   For a given gas, the number of moles present in a sample is directly proportional to the mass of the sample. The problem therefore can be solved even though the gas is not identified (so that its molar mass is not known).

$$23.2 \text{ g} \times \frac{10.4 \text{ L}}{93.2 \text{ L}} = 2.59 \text{ g}$$

130.   a. $V = 21.2 \text{ mL} = 0.0212 \text{ L}$

$$T = \frac{PV}{nR} = \frac{(1.034 \text{ atm})(0.0212 \text{ L})}{(0.00432 \text{ mol})(0.08206 \text{ L atm mol}^{-1} \text{ K}^{-1})} = 61.8 \text{ K}$$

      b. $V = 1.73 \text{ mL} = 0.00173 \text{ L}$

$$P = \frac{nRT}{V} = \frac{(0.000115 \text{ mol})(0.08206 \text{ L atm mol}^{-1} \text{ K}^{-1})(182 \text{ K})}{(0.00173 \text{ L})} = 0.993 \text{ atm}$$

c. $P = 1.23$ mm Hg $= 0.00162$ atm; $T = 152°C + 273 = 425$ K

$$V = \frac{nRT}{P} = \frac{(0.773 \text{ mol})(0.08206 \text{ L atm mol}^{-1} \text{ K}^{-1})(425 \text{ K})}{(0.00162 \text{ atm})} = 1.66 \times 10^4 \text{ L}$$

132. $27°C + 273 = 300$ K

The number of moles of gas it takes to fill the 100. L tanks to 120 atm at 27°C is independent of the identity of the gas.

$$n = \frac{PV}{RT} = \frac{(120 \text{ atm})(100. \text{ L})}{(0.08206 \text{ L atm mol}^{-1} \text{ K}^{-1})(300 \text{ K})} = = 487 \text{ mol}$$

487 mol of *any* gas will fill the tanks to the required specifications.

molar masses: CH_4, 16.0 g; N_2, 28.0 g; CO_2, 44.0 g

for CH_4: (487 mol)(16.0 g/mol) = 7792 g = 7.79 kg CH_4

for N_2: (487 mol)(28.0 g/mol) = 13,636 g = 13.6 kg N_2

for CO_2: (487 mol)(44.0 g/mol) = 21,428 g = 21.4 kg CO_2

134. molar mass of O_2 = 32.00 g; 55 mg = 0.055 g

$$n = 0.055 \text{ g} \times \frac{1 \text{ mol } O_2}{32.00 \text{ g } O_2} = 0.0017 \text{ mol}$$

$V = 100.$ mL $= 0.100$ L; $T = 26°C + 273 = 299$ K

$$P = \frac{nRT}{V} = \frac{(0.0017 \text{ mol})(0.08206 \text{ L atm mol}^{-1} \text{ K}^{-1})(299 \text{ K})}{(0.100 \text{ L})} = 0.42 \text{ atm}$$

136. $P_1 = 1.13$ atm $\qquad\qquad\qquad\qquad P_2 = 1.89$ atm

$V_1 = 100$ mL $= 0.100$ L $\qquad\qquad V_2 = 500$ mL $= 0.500$ L

$T_1 = 300$ K $\qquad\qquad\qquad\qquad\quad T_2 = ?$

$$T_2 = \frac{T_1 P_2 V_2}{P_1 V_1} = \frac{(300 \text{ K})(1.89 \text{ atm})(0.500 \text{ L})}{(1.13 \text{ atm})(0.100 \text{ L})} = 2.51 \times 10^3 \text{ K}$$

Note that the calculation could have been carried through with the two volumes expressed in milliliters because the universal gas constant does not appear explicitly in this form of the ideal gas equation.

138. molar masses: N_2, 28.02 g; He, 4.003 g; STP: 1.00 atm, 273 K

$$12.1 \text{ g } N_2 \times \frac{1 \text{ mol } N_2}{28.02 \text{ g } N_2} = 0.432 \text{ mol } N_2$$

$$4.05 \text{ g He} \times \frac{1 \text{ mol He}}{4.003 \text{ g He}} = 1.01 \text{ mol He}$$

…moles of gas = 0.432 mol + 1.01 mol = 1.44 mol

$$\frac{RT}{} = \frac{(1.44 \text{ mol})(0.08206 \text{ L atm mol}^{-1} \text{ K}^{-1})(273 \text{ K})}{(1.00 \text{ atm})} = 32.3 \text{ L}$$

140.   …$NH_3(g)$

…: 11°C + 273 = 284 K

…NH_3 to be produced

…mol N_2 required

…= 0.441 mol H_2 required

$$\frac{\text{…7 mol})(0.08206 \text{ L atm mol}^{-1} \text{ K}^{-1})(284 \text{ K})}{(0.998 \text{ atm})} = 3.43 \text{ L N}_2$$

$$\frac{}{P} = \frac{(0.441 \text{ mol})(0.08206 \text{ L atm mol}^{-1} \text{ K}^{-1})(284 \text{ K})}{(0.998 \text{ atm})} = 10.3 \text{ L H}_2$$

…$(s) + 3O_2(g) \rightarrow 2Cu_2O(s) + 2SO_2(g)$

…olar mass Cu_2S = 159.2 g; 27.5°C + 273 = 301 K

$$25 \text{ g Cu}_2\text{S} \times \frac{1 \text{ mol Cu}_2\text{S}}{159.2 \text{ g Cu}_2\text{S}} = 0.1570 \text{ mol Cu}_2\text{S}$$

$$0.1570 \text{ mol Cu}_2\text{S} \times \frac{3 \text{ mol O}_2}{2 \text{ mol Cu}_2\text{S}} = 0.2355 \text{ mol O}_2$$

$$V_{\text{oxygen}} = \frac{nRT}{P} = \frac{(0.2355 \text{ mol})(0.08206 \text{ L atm mol}^{-1} \text{ K}^{-1})(301 \text{ K})}{(0.998 \text{ atm})} = 5.8 \text{ L O}_2$$

$$0.1570 \text{ mol Cu}_2\text{S} \times \frac{2 \text{ mol SO}_2}{2 \text{ mol Cu}_2\text{S}} = 0.1570 \text{ mol SO}_2$$

$$V_{\text{sulfur dioxide}} = \frac{nRT}{P} = \frac{(0.1570 \text{ mol})(0.08206 \text{ L atm mol}^{-1} \text{ K}^{-1})(301 \text{ K})}{(0.998 \text{ atm})} = 3.9 \text{ L SO}_2$$

144.   One mole of any ideal gas occupies 22.4 L at STP.

$$35 \text{ mol N}_2 \times \frac{22.4 \text{ L}}{1 \text{ mol}} = 7.8 \times 10^2 \text{ L}$$

146.   molar masses: He, 4.003 g; Ar, 39.95 g; Ne, 20.18 g

$$5.0 \text{ g He} \times \frac{1 \text{ mol He}}{4.003 \text{ g He}} = 1.249 \text{ mol He}$$

$$1.0 \text{ g Ar} \times \frac{1 \text{ mol Ar}}{39.95 \text{ g Ar}} = 0.02503 \text{ mol Ar}$$

$$3.5 \text{ g Ne} \times \frac{1 \text{ mol Ne}}{20.18 \text{ g Ne}} = 0.1734 \text{ mol Ne}$$

Total moles of gas = 1.249 + 0.02503 + 0.1734 = 1.447 mol

22.4 L is the volume occupied by one mole of any ideal gas at STP. This would apply even if the gas sample is a *mixture* of individual gases.

$$1.447 \text{ mol} \times \frac{22.4 \text{ L}}{1 \text{ mol}} = 32 \text{ L total volume for the mixture}$$

The *partial pressure* of each individual gas in the mixture will be related to what *fraction* on a mole basis each gas represents in the mixture.

$$P_{He} = 1.00 \text{ atm} \times \frac{1.249 \text{ mol He}}{1.447 \text{ mol total}} = 0.86 \text{ atm}$$

$$P_{Ar} = 1.00 \text{ atm} \times \frac{0.02503 \text{ mol Ar}}{1.447 \text{ mol total}} = 0.017 \text{ atm}$$

$$P_{Ne} = 1.00 \text{ atm} \times \frac{0.1734 \text{ mol Ne}}{1.447 \text{ mol total}} = 0.12 \text{ atm}$$

148.   The solution is only 50% H_2O_2. Therefore 125 g solution = 62.5 g H_2O_2

molar mass of H_2O_2 = 34.02 g; $T = 27°C = 300$ K; $P = 764$ mm Hg = 1.01 atm

$$62.5 \text{ g } H_2O_2 \times \frac{1 \text{ mol}}{34.02 \text{ g}} = 1.84 \text{ mol } H_2O_2$$

$$1.84 \text{ mol } H_2O_2 \times \frac{1 \text{ mol } O_2}{2 \text{ mol } H_2O_2} = 0.920 \text{ mol } O_2$$

$$V = \frac{nRT}{P} = \frac{(0.920 \text{ mol})(0.08206 \text{ L atm mol}^{-1} \text{ K}^{-1})(300 \text{ K})}{(1.01 \text{ atm})} = 22.4 \text{ L}$$

CUMULATIVE REVIEW

Chapters 13–15

2.   The pressure of the atmosphere represents the mass of the gases in the atmosphere pressing down on the surface of the earth. The device most commonly used to measure the pressure of the atmosphere is the mercury barometer shown in Figure 13.2 in the text.

A simple experiment to demonstrate the pressure of the atmosphere is shown in Figure 13.1 in the text. Some water is added to a metal can, and the can heated until the water boils (boiling represents when the pressure of the vapor coming from the water is equal to the atmospheric pressure). The can is then stoppered. As the steam in the can cools, it condenses to liquid water, which lowers the pressure of gas inside the can. The pressure of the atmosphere outside the can is then much larger than the pressure inside the can, and the can collapses.

4.   In simple terms, Boyle's law states that the volume of a gas sample will decrease if you squeeze harder on it. Imagine squeezing hard on a tennis ball with your hand: the ball collapses as the gas inside is forced into a smaller volume by your hand. Of course, to be perfectly correct, the temperature and amount of gas (moles) must remain the same as you adjust the pressure for Boyle's law to hold true. There are two mathematical statements of Boyle's law you should remember. The first is

$$P \times V = \text{constant},$$

which basically is the definition of Boyle's law (in order for the product ($P \times V$) to remain constant, if one of these terms increases the other must decrease). The second formula is the one more commonly used in solving problems,

$$P_1 \times V_1 = P_2 \times V_2.$$

With this second formulation, we can determine pressure-volume information about a given sample under two sets of conditions. These two mathematical formulas are just two different ways of saying the same thing: if the pressure on a sample of gas is increased, the volume of the sample of gas will decrease. A graph of Boyle's law data is given as Figure 13.5: this type of graph ($xy = k$) is known to mathematicians as a hyperbola.

6.   Charles's law simply says that if you heat a sample of gas, the volume of the sample will increase. That is, when the temperature of a gas is increased, the volume of the gas also increases (assuming the pressure and amount of gas remains the same). Charles's law is a direct proportionality when the temperature is expressed in kelvins (if you increase T, this increases V), whereas Boyle's law is an inverse proportionality (if you increase P, this decreases V). There are two mathematical statements of Charles's law with which you should be familiar. The first statement is:

$$V = kT.$$

This is simply a definition (the volume of a gas sample is directly related to its Kelvin temperature: if you increase the temperature, the volume increases). The working formulation of Charles's law we use in problem solving is given as:

$$\frac{V_1}{T_1} = \frac{V_2}{T_2}$$

With this formulation, we can determine volume-temperature information for a given gas sample under two sets of conditions. Charles's law only holds true if the amount of gas remains the same (obviously the volume of a gas sample would increase if there were more gas present) and also if the pressure remains the same (a change in pressure also changes the volume of a gas sample).

8.   Avogadro's law tells us that, with all other things being equal, two moles of gas are twice as big as one mole of gas! That is, the volume of a sample of gas is directly proportional to the number of moles or molecules of gas present (at constant temperature and pressure). If we want to compare the volumes of two samples of the same gas as an indication of the amount of gas present in the samples, we would have to make certain that the two samples of gas are at the same pressure and temperature: the volume of a sample of gas would vary with either temperature or pressure, or both. Avogadro's law holds true for comparing gas samples that are under the same conditions. Avogadro's law is a direct proportionality: the greater the number of gas molecules you have in a sample, the larger the sample's volume will be.

10.   The "partial" pressure of an individual gas in a mixture of gases represents the pressure the gas would have in the same container at the same temperature if it were the only gas present. The total pressure in a mixture of gases is the sum of the individual partial pressures of the gases present in the mixture. Because the partial pressures of the gases in a mixture are additive (i.e., the total pressure is the sum of the partial pressures), this suggests that the total pressure in a container is a function only of the number of molecules present in the same, and not of the identity of the molecules or any other property of the molecules (such as their inherent atomic size).

12.   The main postulates of the kinetic-molecular theory for gases are as follows: (a) gases consist of tiny particles (atoms or molecules), and the size of these particles is negligible compared to the bulk volume of a gas sample; (b) the particles in a gas are in constant random motion, colliding with each other and with the walls of the container; (c) the particles in a gas sample do not exert any attractive or repulsive forces on one another; (d) the average kinetic energy of the particles in a sample of gas is directly related to the absolute temperature of the gas sample. The pressure exerted by a gas is a result of the molecules colliding with (and pushing on) the walls of the container. The pressure increases with temperature because at a higher temperature, the molecules are moving faster and hit the walls of the container with greater force. A gas fills whatever volume is available to it because the molecules in a gas are in constant random motion: if the motion of the molecules is random, they eventually will move out into whatever volume is available until the distribution of molecules is uniform. At constant pressure, the volume of a gas sample increases as the temperature is increased because with each collision having greater force, the container must expand so that the molecules (and therefore the collisions) are farther apart if the pressure is to remain constant.

14.   Solids and liquids are much more condensed states of matter than are gases: the molecules are much closer together in solids and liquids and interact with each other to a much greater extent. Solids and liquids have much greater densities than do gases, and are much less compressible, because there is so little room between the molecules in the solid and liquid states (solids and liquids effectively have native volumes of their own, and their volumes are not affected nearly as much by the temperature or pressure). Although solids are more rigid than liquids, the solid and liquid state have much more in common with each other than either of these states has with the gaseous state. We know this is true because it typically only takes a few kilojoules of energy to

melt 1 mol of a solid (not much change has to take place in the molecules), whereas it may take 10 times more energy to vaporize a liquid (as there is a great change between the liquid and gaseous states).

16.   The normal boiling point of water, that is, water's boiling point at a pressure of exactly 760 mm Hg, is 100°C (you will recall that the boiling point of water was used to set one of the reference temperatures of the Celsius temperature scale). Water remains at 100°C while boiling, until all the water has boiled away, because the additional heat energy being added to the sample is used to overcome attractive forces among the water molecules as they go from the condensed, liquid state to the gaseous state. The normal (760 mm Hg) freezing point of water is exactly 0°C (again, this property of water was used as one of the reference points for the Celsius temperature scale). A cooling curve for water is given in Figure 14.2. Notice how the curve shows that the amount of heat needed to boil the sample is much larger than the amount needed to melt the sample.

18.   Dipole-dipole forces are a type of intermolecular force that can exist between molecules with permanent dipole moments. Molecules with permanent dipole moments try to orient themselves so that the positive end of one polar molecule can attract the negative end of another polar molecule. Dipole-dipole forces are not nearly as strong as ionic or covalent bonding forces (only about 1% as strong as covalent bonding forces) because electrostatic attraction is related to the magnitude of the charges of the attracting species. As polar molecules have only a "partial" charge at each end of the dipole, the magnitude of the attractive force is not as large. The strength of such forces also drops rapidly as molecules become farther apart and is important only in the solid and liquid states (such forces are negligible in the gaseous state because the molecules are too far apart). Hydrogen bonding is an especially strong sort of dipole-dipole attractive force that can exist when hydrogen atoms are directly bonded to the most strongly electronegative atoms (N, O, and F). Because the hydrogen atom is so small, dipoles involving N–H, O–H, and F–H bonds can approach each other much more closely than can dipoles involving other atoms. As the magnitude of dipole-dipole forces is dependent on distance, unusually strong attractive forces can exist in such molecules. We take the fact that the boiling point of water is higher than that of the other covalent hydrogen compounds of the Group 6 elements as evidence for the special strength of hydrogen bonding (it takes more energy to vaporize water because of the extra strong forces holding together the molecules in the liquid state).

20.   Vaporization of a liquid requires an input of energy because the intermolecular forces that hold the molecules together in the liquid state must be overcome. The high heat of vaporization of water is essential to life on Earth because much of the excess energy striking the Earth from the sun is dissipated in vaporizing water. Condensation is the opposite process to vaporization; that is, condensation refers to the process by which molecules in the vapor state form a liquid. In a closed container containing a liquid and some empty space above the liquid, an equilibrium is set up between vaporization and condensation. The liquid in such a sealed container never completely evaporates: when the liquid is first placed in the container, the liquid phase begins to evaporate into the empty space. As the number of molecules in the vapor phase begins to get large, however, some of these molecules begin to re-enter the liquid phase. Eventually, every time a molecule of liquid somewhere in the container enters the vapor phase, somewhere else in the container a molecule of vapor re-enters the liquid. There is no further net change in the amount of liquid phase (although molecules are continually moving between the liquid and vapor phases). The pressure of the vapor in such an equilibrium situation is characteristic for the liquid at each particular temperature (for example, the vapor pressures of water are tabulated at different temperatures in Table 13.2). A simple experiment to determine vapor pressure is shown in Figure 14.10. Samples of a liquid are injected into a sealed tube containing mercury; because mercury is so dense, the liquids float to the top of the mercury where they evaporate. As the vapor pressures

of the liquids develop to the saturation point, the level of mercury in the tube changes as an index of the magnitude of the vapor pressures. Typically, liquids with strong intermolecular forces have small vapor pressures (they have more difficulty in evaporating) than do liquids with very weak intermolecular forces: for example, the components of gasoline (weak forces) have much higher vapor pressures, and evaporate more easily than does water (strong forces).

22. The simple model we use to explain many properties of metallic elements is called the electron sea model. In this model we picture a regular lattice array of metal cations in sort of a "sea" of mobile valence electrons. The electrons can move easily to conduct heat or electricity through the metal; and the lattice of cations can be deformed fairly easily, allowing the metal to be hammered into a sheet or stretched to make a wire. An alloy contains a mixture of elements, which overall has metallic properties. Substitutional alloys consist of a host metal in which some of the atoms in the metal's crystalline structure are replaced by atoms of other metallic elements of comparable size to the atoms of the host metal. For example, sterling silver consists of an alloy in which approximately 7% of the silver atoms have been replaced by copper atoms. Brass and pewter are also substitutional alloys. An interstitial alloy is formed when other smaller atoms enter the interstices (holes) between atoms in the host metal's crystal structure. Steel is an interstitial alloy in which typically carbon atoms enter the interstices of a crystal of iron atoms. The presence of the interstitial carbon atoms markedly changes the properties of the iron, making it much harder, more malleable, and more ductile. Depending on the amount of carbon introduced into the iron crystals, the properties of the resulting steel can be carefully controlled.

24. A saturated solution is one that contains as much solute as can dissolve at a particular temperature. To say that a solution is saturated does not necessarily mean that the solute is present at a high concentration. For example, magnesium hydroxide only dissolves to a very small extent before the solution is saturated, whereas it takes a great deal of sugar to form a saturated solution (and the saturated solution is extremely concentrated). A saturated solution is one which is in equilibrium with undissolved solute: as molecules of solute dissolve from the solid in one place in the solution, dissolved molecules rejoin the solid phase in another place in the solution. As with the development of vapor pressure above a liquid (see Question 20 above), formation of a solution reaches a state of dynamic equilibrium: once the rates of dissolving and "undissolving" become equal, there will be no further net change in the concentration of the solution and the solution will be saturated.

26. Adding more solvent to a solution so as to dilute the solution *does not change* the number of moles of solute present, but only changes the volume in which the solute is dispersed. If we are using the molarity of the solution to describe its concentration, the number of liters is changed when we add solvent, and the number of moles per liter (the molarity) changes, but the actual number of moles of solute does not change. For example, 125 mL of 0.551 M NaCl contains 68.9 millimol of NaCl. The solution will still contain 68.9 millimol of NaCl after the 250 mL of water is added to it, only now the 68.9 millimol of NaCl will be dispersed in a total volume of 375 mL. This gives the new molarity as 68.9 mmol/375 mL = 0.184 M. The volume and the concentration have changed, but the number of moles of solute in the solution has not changed.

28. $P_1 \times V_1 = P_2 \times V_2$

a. $$V_2 = \frac{P_1 \times V_1}{P_2} = \frac{125 \text{ mL} \times 755 \text{ mm Hg}}{899 \text{ mm Hg}} = 105 \text{ mL}$$

b. $$P_2 = \frac{P_1 \times V_1}{V_2} = \frac{455 \text{ mL} \times 755 \text{ mm Hg}}{327 \text{ mL}} = 1.05 \times 10^3 \text{ mm Hg}$$

30.   a. $PV = nRT$; molar mass He = 4.003 g; 25°C = 298 K

$1.15 \text{ g He} \times \dfrac{1 \text{ mol}}{4.003 \text{ g}} = 0.2873 \text{ mol He}$

$V = \dfrac{nRT}{P} = \dfrac{(0.2873 \text{ mol})(0.08206 \text{ L-atm/mol-K})(298 \text{ K})}{(1.01 \text{ atm})} = 6.96 \text{ L}$

   b.   molar masses: H_2, 2.016 g; He, 4.003 g; 0°C = 273 K

$2.27 \text{ g } H_2 \times \dfrac{1 \text{ mol } H_2}{2.016 \text{ g } H_2} = 1.126 \text{ mol } H_2$

$1.03 \text{ g He} \times \dfrac{1 \text{ mol He}}{4.003 \text{ g He}} = 0.2573 \text{ mol He}$

$P_{H_2} = \dfrac{nRT}{V} = \dfrac{(1.126 \text{ mol } H_2)(0.08206 \text{ L-atm/mol-K})(273 \text{ K})}{(5.00 \text{ L})} = 5.05 \text{ atm}$

$P_{He} = \dfrac{nRT}{V} = \dfrac{(0.2573 \text{ mol He})(0.08206 \text{ L-atm/mol-K})(273 \text{ K})}{(5.00 \text{ L})} = 1.15 \text{ atm}$

   c.   molar mass of Ar = 39.95 g; 27°C = 300 K

$42.5 \text{ g Ar} \times \dfrac{1 \text{ mol Ar}}{39.95 \text{ g Ar}} = 1.064 \text{ mol Ar}$

$P = \dfrac{nRT}{V} = \dfrac{(1.064 \text{ mol Ar})(0.08206 \text{ L-atm/mol-K})(300 \text{ K})}{(9.97 \text{ L})} = 2.63 \text{ atm}$

32.   molar masses: $CaCO_3$, 100.09 g; CO_2, 44.01 g

$1.25 \text{ g } CaCO_3 \times \dfrac{1 \text{ mol } CaCO_3}{100.09 \text{ g}} = 0.01249 \text{ mol } CaCO_3$

$0.01249 \text{ mol } CaCO_3 \times \dfrac{1 \text{ mol } CO_2}{1 \text{ mol } CaCO_3} = 0.01249 \text{ mol } CO_2$

$0.01249 \text{ mol } CO_2 \times \dfrac{44.01 \text{ g } CO_2}{1 \text{ mol } CO_2} = 0.550 \text{ g } CO_2$

$0.01249 \text{ mol } CO_2 \times \dfrac{22.4 \text{ L}}{1 \text{ mol}} = 0.280 \text{ L } CO_2 \text{ at STP}$

34.   a.   mass of solution = 2.05 g NaCl + 19.2 g water = 21.25 g solution

$\dfrac{2.05 \text{ g NaCl}}{21.25 \text{ g solution}} \times 100 = 9.65\% \text{ NaCl}$

b. $26.2 \text{ g solution} \times \dfrac{10.5 \text{ g CaCl}_2}{100 \text{ g solution}} = 2.75 \text{ g CaCl}_2$

c. $225 \text{ g solution} \times \dfrac{5.05 \text{ g NaCl}}{100 \text{ g solution}} = 11.4 \text{ g NaCl required}$

36. $M_1 \times V_1 = M_2 \times V_2$

a. $M_2 = \dfrac{(12.5 \text{ mL})(1.515 \text{ } M)}{(12.5 + 25 \text{ mL})} = 0.505 \text{ } (0.51) \text{ } M$

b. $M_2 = \dfrac{(75.0 \text{ mL})(0.252 \text{ } M)}{(225 \text{ mL})} = 0.0840 \text{ } M$

c. $M_2 = \dfrac{(52.1 \text{ mL})(0.751 \text{ } M)}{(52.1 + 250. \text{ mL})} = 0.130 \text{ } M$

38. a. $125 \text{ mL solution} \times \dfrac{1.84 \text{ g solution}}{1 \text{ mL solution}} = 230. \text{ g solution}$

$230. \text{ g solution} \times \dfrac{98.3 \text{ g H}_2\text{SO}_4}{1 \text{ g solution}} = 226 \text{ g H}_2\text{SO}_4$

b. The concentrated solution contains 226 g of H_2SO_4 (molar mass 98.09 g) in 125 mL (0.125 L) of solution

$226 \text{ g H}_2\text{SO}_4 \times \dfrac{1 \text{ mol H}_2\text{SO}_4}{98.09 \text{ g H}_2\text{SO}_4} = 2.304 \text{ mol H}_2\text{SO}_4$

$M = \dfrac{2.304 \text{ mol H}_2\text{SO}_4}{0.125 \text{ L solution}} = 18.4 \text{ } M$

c. $M_1 \times V_1 = M_2 \times V_2$

$M_2 = \dfrac{(0.125 \text{ L})(18.4 \text{ } M)}{3.01 \text{ L}} = 0.764 \text{ } M$

d. $\dfrac{0.764 \text{ mol}}{1 \text{ L}} \times \dfrac{2 \text{ equivalents}}{1 \text{ mol}} = 1.53 \text{ } N$

e. $\text{mmol NaOH} = 45.3 \text{ mL} \times \dfrac{0.532 \text{ mmol NaOH}}{1 \text{ mL}} = 24.10 \text{ mmol}$

$H_2SO_4 + 2NaOH \rightarrow Na_2SO_4 + 2H_2O$

$\text{mmol H}_2\text{SO}_4 \text{ required} = 24.10 \text{ mmol NaOH} \times \dfrac{1 \text{ mmol H}_2\text{SO}_4}{2 \text{ mmol NaOH}} = 12.05 \text{ mmol H}_2\text{SO}_4$

$12.05 \text{ mmol H}_2\text{SO}_4 \times \dfrac{1 \text{ mL solution}}{0.764 \text{ mmol H}_2\text{SO}_4} = 15.8 \text{ mL of the sulfuric acid solution.}$

CHAPTER 16

Acids and Bases

2. $HCl(g) \xrightarrow{H_2O} H^+(aq) + Cl^-(aq)$

       $NaOH(s) \xrightarrow{H_2O} Na^+(aq) + OH^-(aq)$

4.   Conjugate acid–base pairs differ from each other by one proton (one hydrogen ion, H^+). For example, CH_3COOH (acetic acid), differs from its conjugate base, CH_3COO^- (acetate ion), by a single H^+ ion.

       $CH_3COOH(aq) \rightleftharpoons CH_3COO^-(aq) + H^+(aq)$

6.   In addition to sodium bicarbonate, the gum also contains citric acid and malic acid. When the gum is exposed to moisture in the mouth, the bicarbonate ion behaves as a *base* and reacts with hydrogen ion from the acids: $H^+(aq) + HCO_3^-(aq) \rightarrow H_2O(l) + CO_2(g)$

8.   a.   a conjugate pair: the two species differ by one proton

       b.   a conjugate pair: the two species differ by one proton

       c.   a conjugate pair: the two species differ by one proton

       d.   not a conjugate pair

              H_2O, OH^-

              OH^-, O^{2-}

10.   a. $NH_3(aq)(base) + H_2O(l)(acid) \rightleftharpoons NH_4^+(aq)(acid) + OH^-(aq)(base)$

       b. $NH_4^+(aq)(acid) + H_2O(l)(base) \rightleftharpoons NH_3(aq)(base) + H_3O^+(aq)(acid)$

       c. $NH_2^-(aq)(base) + H_2O(l)(acid) \rightleftharpoons NH_3(aq)(acid) + OH^-(aq)(base)$

12.   The conjugate *acid* of the species indicated would have *one additional proton*:

       a.   HClO

       b.   HCl

       c. $HClO_3$

       d. $HClO_4$

14.   The conjugate *bases* of the species indicated would have *one less proton*:

       a. BrO^-

       b. HSO_3^-

       c. SO_3^{2-}

       d. CH_3NH_2

16.   a. $O^{2-}(aq) + H_2O(l) \rightleftharpoons OH^-(aq) + OH^-(aq)$

      b. $NH_3(aq) + H_2O(l) \rightleftharpoons NH_4^+(aq) + OH^-(aq)$

      c. $HSO_4^-(aq) + H_2O(l) \rightleftharpoons SO_4^{2-}(aq) + H_3O^+(aq)$

      d. $HNO_2(aq) + H_2O(l) \rightleftharpoons NO_2^-(aq) + H_3O^+(aq)$

18.   To say that an acid is *weak* in aqueous solution means that the acid does not easily transfer protons to water (and does not fully ionize). If an acid does not lose protons easily, then the acid's anion must be a strong attractor of protons (good at holding on to protons).

20.   A strong acid is one that loses its protons easily and fully ionizes in water; this means that the acid's conjugate base must be poor at attracting and holding on to protons, and is therefore a relatively weak base. A weak acid is one that resists loss of its protons and does not ionize well in water; this means that the acid's conjugate base attracts and holds onto protons tightly and is a relatively strong base.

22. H_2SO_4 (sulfuric): $H_2SO_4 + H_2O \rightarrow HSO_4^- + H_3O^+$

      HCl (hydrochloric): $HCl + H_2O \rightarrow Cl^- + H_3O^+$

      HNO_3 (nitric): $HNO_3 + H_2O \rightarrow NO_3^- + H_3O^+$

      $HClO_4$ (perchloric): $HClO_4 + H_2O \rightarrow ClO_4^- + H_3O^+$

24.   An oxyacid is an acid containing a particular element which is bonded to one or more oxygen atoms. HNO_3, H_2SO_4, $HClO_4$ are oxyacids. HCl, HF, HBr are not oxyacids.

26.   Salicylic acid is a monoprotic acid: only the hydrogen of the carboxyl group ionizes.

28.   For example, HCO_3^- can behave as an acid if it reacts with something that more strongly gains protons than does HCO_3^- itself. For example, HCO_3^- would behave as an acid when reacting with hydroxide ion (a much stronger base).

      $HCO_3^-(aq) + OH^-(aq) \rightarrow CO_3^{2-}(aq) + H_2O(l)$.

On the other hand, HCO_3^- would behave as a base when reacted with something that more readily loses protons than does HCO_3^- itself. For example, HCO_3^- would behave as a base when reacting with hydrochloric acid (a much stronger acid).

      $HCO_3^-(aq) + HCl(aq) \rightarrow H_2CO_3(aq) + Cl^-(aq)$

For $H_2PO_4^-$, similar equations can be written:

      $H_2PO_4^-(aq) + OH^-(aq) \rightarrow HPO_4^{2-}(aq) + H_2O(l)$

      $H_2PO_4^-(aq) + H_3O^+(aq) \rightarrow H_3PO_4(aq) + H_2O(l)$

30.   The hydrogen ion concentration and the hydroxide ion concentration of water are *not* independent: they are related by the equilibrium

$$H_2O(l) \rightleftharpoons H^+(aq) + OH^-(aq)$$

for which $K_w = [H^+][OH^-] = 1.0 \times 10^{-14}$ at 25°C.

If the concentration of one of these ions is increased by addition of a reagent producing H^+ or OH^-, then the concentration of the complementary ion will have to decrease so that the value of K_w will hold true. So if an acid is added to a solution, the concentration of hydroxide ion in the solution will decrease to a lower value. Similarly, if a base is added to a solution, then the concentration of hydrogen ion will have to decrease to a lower value.

32. $K_w = [H^+][OH^-] = 1.0 \times 10^{-14}$ at 25°C

   a. $[H^+] = \dfrac{1.0 \times 10^{-14}}{3.44 \times 10^{-1}\,M} = 2.9 \times 10^{-14}\,M$; solution is basic

   b. $[H^+] = \dfrac{1.0 \times 10^{-14}}{9.79 \times 10^{-11}\,M} = 1.0 \times 10^{-4}\,M$; solution is acidic

   c. $[H^+] = \dfrac{1.0 \times 10^{-14}}{4.89 \times 10^{-6}\,M} = 2.0 \times 10^{-9}\,M$; solution is basic

   d. $[H^+] = \dfrac{1.0 \times 10^{-14}}{3.78 \times 10^{-7}\,M} = 2.6 \times 10^{-8}\,M$; solution is basic

34. $K_w = [H^+][OH^-] = 1.0 \times 10^{-14}$ at 25°C

   a. $[OH^-] = \dfrac{1.0 \times 10^{-14}}{1.02 \times 10^{-7}\,M} = 9.8 \times 10^{-8}\,M$; solution is acidic

   b. $[OH^-] = \dfrac{1.0 \times 10^{-14}}{9.77 \times 10^{-8}\,M} = 1.02 \times 10^{-7}\,M\,(1.0 \times 10^{-7}\,M)$; solution is slightly basic

   c. $[OH^-] = \dfrac{1.0 \times 10^{-14}}{3.41 \times 10^{-3}\,M} = 2.9 \times 10^{-12}\,M$; solution is acidic

   d. $[OH^-] = \dfrac{1.0 \times 10^{-14}}{4.79 \times 10^{-11}\,M} = 2.1 \times 10^{-4}\,M$; solution is basic

36.   a. $[OH^-] = 6.03 \times 10^{-4}\,M$ is more basic

   b. $[OH^-] = 4.21 \times 10^{-6}\,M$ is more basic

   c. $[OH^-] = 8.04 \times 10^{-4}\,M$ is more basic

38.   Answer depends on student choice.

40.   pH 1–2, deep red; pH 4, purple; pH 8, blue; pH 11, green

42. $pH = -\log[H^+]$

    a. $pH = -\log[9.35 \times 10^{-2} \ M] = 1.029$; solution is acidic

    b. $pH = -\log[3.75 \times 10^{-4} \ M] = 3.426$; solution is acidic

    c. $pH = -\log[8.36 \times 10^{-6} \ M] = 5.078$; solution is acidic

    d. $pH = -\log[5.42 \times 10^{-8} \ M] = 7.266$; solution is basic

44. $pOH = -\log[OH^-]$ $pH = 14.00 - pOH$

    a. $pOH = -\log[8.63 \times 10^{-3} \ M] = 2.064$

         $pH = 14.00 - 2.064 = 11.936 = 11.94$; solution is basic

    b. $pOH = -\log[7.44 \times 10^{-6} \ M] = 5.128$

         $pH = 14.00 - 5.128 = 8.872 = 8.87$; solution is basic

    c. $pOH = -\log[9.35 \times 10^{-9} \ M] = 8.029$

         $pH = 14.00 - 8.029 = 5.971 = 5.97$; solution is acidic

    d. $pOH = -\log[1.21 \times 10^{-11} \ M] = 10.917$

         $pH = 14.00 - 10.917 = 3.083 = 3.08$; solution is acidic

46. $pOH = 14.00 - pH$

    a. $pOH = 14.00 - 9.78 = 4.22$; solution is basic

    b. $pOH = 14.00 - 4.01 = 9.99$; solution is acidic

    c. $pOH = 14.00 - 2.79 = 11.21$; solution is acidic

    d. $pOH = 14.00 - 11.21 = 2.79$; solution is basic

48.   a. $pH = -\log[1.91 \times 10^{-2} \ M] = 1.719$; solution is acidic

$$[OH^-] = \frac{1.0 \times 10^{-14}}{1.91 \times 10^{-2} \ M} = 5.2 \times 10^{-13} \ M$$

    b. $pH = -\log[4.83 \times 10^{-7} \ M] = 6.316$; solution is acidic

$$[OH^-] = \frac{1.0 \times 10^{-14}}{4.83 \times 10^{-7} \ M} = 2.1 \times 10^{-8} \ M$$

    c. $pH = -\log[8.92 \times 10^{-11} \ M] = 10.050$; solution is basic

$$[OH^-] = \frac{1.0 \times 10^{-14}}{8.92 \times 10^{-11} \ M} = 1.1 \times 10^{-4} \ M$$

    d. $pH = -\log[6.14 \times 10^{-5} \ M] = 4.212$; solution is acidic

$$[OH^-] = \frac{1.0 \times 10^{-14}}{6.14 \times 10^{-5} \ M} = 1.6 \times 10^{-10} \ M$$

50. $[H^+] = \{inv\}\{log\}[-pH]$ or 10^{-pH}

    a. $[H^+] = \{inv\}\{log\}[-11.21] = 6.2 \times 10^{-12}\ M$

    b. $[H^+] = \{inv\}\{log\}[-4.39] = 4.1 \times 10^{-5}\ M$

    c. $[H^+] = \{inv\}\{log\}[-7.44] = 3.6 \times 10^{-8}\ M$

    d. $[H^+] = \{inv\}\{log\}[-1.38] = 4.2 \times 10^{-2}\ M$

52. $pH + pOH = 14.00$ $[H^+] = \{inv\}\{log\}[-pH]$ or 10^{-pH}

    a. $pH = 14.00 - 4.99 = 9.01$

        $[H^+] = \{inv\}\{log\}[-9.01] = 9.8 \times 10^{-10}\ M$

    b. $[H^+] = \{inv\}\{log\}[-7.74] = 1.8 \times 10^{-8}\ M$

    c. $pH = 14.00 - 10.74 = 3.26$

        $[H^+] = \{inv\}\{log\}[-3.26] = 5.5 \times 10^{-4}\ M$

    d. $[H^+] = \{inv\}\{log\}[-2.25] = 5.6 \times 10^{-3}\ M$

54.   a. $pH = -log[4.39 \times 10^{-6}\ M] = 5.358$

    b. $pH = 14.00 - pOH = 14.00 - 10.36 = 3.64$

    c. $pOH = -log[9.37 \times 10^{-9}\ M] = 8.028$ $pH = 14.00 - 8.028 = 5.97$

    d. $pH = -log[3.31 \times 10^{-1}\ M] = 0.480$

56.   The solution contains water molecules, H_3O^+ ions (protons), and NO_3^- ions. Because HNO_3 is a strong acid, which is completely ionized in water, there are no HNO_3 molecules present.

58.   a. HNO_3 is a strong acid and completely ionized so $[H^+] = 1.21 \times 10^{-3}\ M$ and $pH = 2.917$.

    b. $HClO_4$ is a strong acid and completely ionized so $[H^+] = 0.000199\ M$ and $pH = 3.701$.

    c. HCl is a strong acid and completely ionized so $[H^+] = 5.01 \times 10^{-5}\ M$ and $pH = 4.300$.

    d. HBr is a strong acid and completely ionized so $[H^+] = 0.00104\ M$ and $pH = 2.983$.

60.   A buffered solution consists of a mixture of a weak acid and its conjugate base; one example of a buffered solution is a mixture of acetic acid (CH_3COOH) and sodium acetate ($NaCH_3COO$).

62.   The weak acid component of a buffered solution is capable of reacting with added strong base. For example, using the buffered solution given as an example in Question 60, acetic acid would consume added sodium hydroxide as follows:

$$CH_3COOH(aq) + NaOH(aq) \rightarrow NaCH_3COO(aq) + H_2O(l).$$

Acetic acid *neutralizes* the added NaOH and prevents it from having much effect on the overall pH of the solution.

64.   HCl: $H_3O^+ + C_2H_3O_2^- \rightarrow HC_2H_3O_2 + H_2O$

    NaOH: $OH^- + HC_2H_3O_2 \rightarrow C_2H_3O_2^- + H_2O$

66.   a.   NaOH is completely ionized, so $[OH^-] = 0.10$ M.

pOH $= -\log[0.10] = 1.00$

pH $= 14.00 - 1.00 = 13.00$

b.   KOH is completely ionized, so $[OH^-] = 2.0 \times 10^{-4}$ M.

pOH $= -\log[2.0 \times 10^{-4}] = 3.70$

pH $= 14.00 - 3.70 = 10.30$

c.   CsOH is completely ionized, so $[OH^-] = 6.2 \times 10^{-3}$ M.

pOH $= -\log[6.2 \times 10^{-3}] = 2.21$

pH $= 14.00 - 2.21 = 11.79$

d.   NaOH is completely ionized, so $[OH^-] = 0.0001$ M.

pOH $= -\log[0.0001] = 4.0$

pH $= 14.00 - 4.0 = 10.0$

68.   b, c, and d

70.   a, c, and e represent strong acids; b and d are typical weak acids.

72.   Ordinarily in calculating the pH of strong acid solutions, the major contribution to the concentration of hydrogen ion present is from the dissolved strong acid; we ordinarily neglect the small amount of hydrogen ion present in such solutions due to the ionization of water. With 1.0×10^{-7} M HCl solution, however, the amount of hydrogen ion present due to the ionization of *water* is *comparable* to that present due to the addition of *acid* (HCl) and must be considered in the calculation of pH.

74.   accepts

76.   base

78.   carboxyl (–COOH) $CH_3COOH + H_2O \rightleftharpoons C_2H_3O_2^- + H_3O^+$

80. 1.0×10^{-14}

82.   higher

84.   pH

86.   weak acid

88.   a. H_2O and OH^- represent a conjugate acid–base pair (H_2O is the acid, having one more proton than the base, OH^-).

b. H_2SO_4 and SO_4^{2-} are *not* a conjugate acid–base pair (they differ by *two* protons). The conjugate base of H_2SO_4 is HSO_4^-; the conjugate acid of SO_4^{2-} is also HSO_4^-.

    c. H_3PO_4 and $H_2PO_4^-$ represent a conjugate acid–base pair (H_3PO_4 is the acid, having one more proton than the base $H_2PO_4^-$).

    d. $HC_2H_3O_2$ and $C_2H_3O_2^-$ represent a conjugate acid–base pair ($HC_2H_3O_2$ is the acid, having one more proton than the base $C_2H_3O_2^-$).

90.   The conjugate *acid* of the species indicated would have *one additional proton*:

    a. NH_4^+

    b. NH_3

    c. H_3O^+

    d. H_2O

92.   When an acid ionizes in water, a proton is released to the water as an H_3O^+ ion:

    a. $CH_3CH_2COOH + H_2O \rightleftharpoons CH_3CH_2COO^- + H_3O^+$

    b. $NH_4^+ + H_2O \rightleftharpoons NH_3 + H_3O^+$

    c. $H_2SO_4 + H_2O \rightarrow HSO_4^- + H_3O^+$

    d. $H_3PO_4 + H_2O \rightleftharpoons H_2PO_4^- + H_3O^+$

94. $K_w = [H^+][OH^-] = 1.0 \times 10^{-14}$ at 25°C

    a. $[H^+] = \dfrac{1.0 \times 10^{-14}}{4.22 \times 10^{-3} \ M} = 2.4 \times 10^{-12} \ M$; solution is basic

    b. $[H^+] = \dfrac{1.0 \times 10^{-14}}{1.01 \times 10^{-13} \ M} = 9.9 \times 10^{-2} \ M$; solution is acidic

    c. $[H^+] = \dfrac{1.0 \times 10^{-14}}{3.05 \times 10^{-7} \ M} = 3.3 \times 10^{-8} \ M$; solution is basic

    d. $[H^+] = \dfrac{1.0 \times 10^{-14}}{6.02 \times 10^{-6} \ M} = 1.7 \times 10^{-9} \ M$; solution is basic

96.   a. $[OH^-] = 0.0000032 \ M$ is more basic

    b. $[OH^-] = 1.54 \times 10^{-8} \ M$ is more basic

    c. $[OH^-] = 4.02 \times 10^{-7} \ M$ is more basic

98. $pOH = -\log[OH^-]$ $pH = 14.00 - pOH$

    a. $pOH = -\log[1.4 \times 10^{-6} \ M] = 5.85$; $pH = 14.00 - 5.85 = 8.15$; solution is basic

    b. $pOH = -\log[9.35 \times 10^{-9} \ M] = 8.029 = 8.03$; $pH = 14.00 - 8.029 = 5.97$; solution is acidic

    c. $pOH = -\log[2.21 \times 10^{-1} \ M] = 0.656 = 0.66$; $pH = 14.00 - 0.656 = 13.34$; solution is basic

    d. $pOH = -\log[7.98 \times 10^{-12} \ M] = 11.10$; $pH = 14.00 - 11.098 = 2.90$; solution is acidic

100.   a. $[OH^-] = \dfrac{1.0 \times 10^{-14}}{5.72 \times 10^{-4} \ M} = 1.75 \times 10^{-11} \ M = 1.8 \times 10^{-11} \ M$

            $pOH = -\log[1.75 \times 10^{-11} \ M] = 10.76$

            $pH = 14.00 - 10.76 = 3.24$

    b. $[H^+] = \dfrac{1.0 \times 10^{-14}}{8.91 \times 10^{-5} \ M} = 1.12 \times 10^{-10} \ M = 1.1 \times 10^{-10} \ M$

            $pH = -\log[1.12 \times 10^{-10} \ M] = 9.95$

            $pOH = 14.00 - 9.95 = 4.05$

    c. $[OH^-] = \dfrac{1.0 \times 10^{-14}}{2.87 \times 10^{-12} \ M} = 3.48 \times 10^{-3} \ M = 3.5 \times 10^{-3} \ M$

            $pOH = -\log[3.48 \times 10^{-3} \ M] = 2.46$

            $pH = 14.00 - 2.46 = 11.54$

    d. $[H^+] = \dfrac{1.0 \times 10^{-14}}{7.22 \times 10^{-8} \ M} = 1.39 \times 10^{-7} \ M = 1.4 \times 10^{-7} \ M$

            $pH = -\log[1.39\times \times 10^{-7} \ M] = 6.86$

            $pOH = 14.00 - 6.86 = 7.14$

102. $pH = 14.00 - pOH$ $[H^+] = \{inv\}\{log\}[-pH]$ or 10^{-pH}

    a. $[H^+] = \{inv\}\{log\}[-5.41] = 3.9 \times 10^{-6} \ M$

    b. $pH = 14.00 - 12.04 = 1.96$ $[H^+] = \{inv\}\{log\}[-1.96] = 1.1 \times 10^{-2} \ M$

    c. $[H^+] = \{inv\}\{log\}[-11.91] = 1.2 \times 10^{-12} \ M$

    d. $pH = 14.00 - 3.89 = 10.11$ $[H^+] = \{inv\}\{log\}[-10.11] = 7.8 \times 10^{-11} \ M$

104.   a. $HClO_4$ is a strong acid and completely ionized so $[H^+] = 1.4 \times 10^{-3} \ M$ and $pH = 2.85$.

    b.   HCl is a strong acid and completely ionized so $[H^+] = 3.0 \times 10^{-5} \ M$ and $pH = 4.52$.

    c. HNO_3 is a strong acid and completely ionized so $[H^+] = 5.0 \times 10^{-2} \ M$ and $pH = 1.30$.

    d.   HCl is a strong acid and completely ionized so $[H^+] = 0.0010 \ M$ and $pH = 3.00$.